PREFACE

This book is based on the proceedings of a conference sponsored by the Department of Health, and planned in collaboration with the Institute of Personnel Management, the CBI, the TUC, HSE, the Department of Employment, ACAS and the Health Education Authority. The conference was held at the Royal College of Physicians, St Andrew's Place, London NW1 on 11 January 1993.

Members of the Conference Planning Committee

Rachel Jenkins (Chair)
Department of Health

Dianah Worman
IPM

Karen Harkness
CBI

Peter Jacques
TUC

Pam Buley
Mike Shepherd
Donald Goodhew
Louise Bridson
Dr Zuberi
Dr Lucas
HSE

Anna Orr
Gill Neville
Alison Rose
DE

Ian Hunter
Campbell Ford
ACAS

Virginia Bovell
HEA

PROMOTING MENTAL HEALTH POLICIES IN THE WORKPLACE

Edited by Rachel Jenkins and Dinah Warman

London : HMSO

Acknowledgements

Special thanks are due to Bill Lisle who designed the cartoon
illustrations on the front cover and in Chapter 1.

The conference was organised by Rosemary McMahon at
Professional Briefings.

List of Contributors

Sir John Cullen
Chairman of the Health and Safety Commission

Virginia Bottomley JP MP
Secretary of State for Health

Howard Davies
Director General, CBI

Alan Tuffin
President, TUC

Dr Barrie Thorpe
Production Director
Zeneca Pharmaceuticals (formerly ICI pharmaceuticals)

Sally Young
Personnel Executive, Mark and Spencers PLC

Dr Eric Teasdale
Medical Officer Zeneca Pharmaceuticals (formerly ICI pharmaceuticals)

Dr Rachel Jenkins
Principal Medical Officer
Mental Health, Elderly and Disability
Department of Health

Michael Craft
Director
Jocelyn Chamberlain Unit for Health Promotion and Disease Prevention
St George's Hospital Medical School

Professor Cary Cooper
Professor of Organisational Psychology
Manchester School of Management

Campbell Ford
Principal
Advisory Conciliation and Arbitration Service – (ACAS)

Professor David Shapiro
MRC/ESRC Social and Applied Psychology Unit
University of Sheffield

Dr Ann Fingret
Consultant Physician in Occupational Medicine
The Royal Marsden Hospital and the Institute of Cancer Research

Patrick McLoughlin MP
Under Secretary of State
Department of Employment

Michael Bett
Deputy Chairman
British Telecom and President Elect, IPM

CONTENTS

Foreword by Sir John Cullen, Chairman, Health and Safety Commission

I am delighted to introduce this publication.

Mental health is an issue of major importance in the workplace today. Stress, anxiety and depression account for an estimated 80 million working days lost each year. The cost to individuals, families and the economy as a whole is potentially huge.

The publication is based on the 'Mental Health at Work' conference which took place on 11 January. It highlights a wide variety of work now being undertaken to promote and safeguard mental health in the workplace. It examines possible strategies for tackling and preventing the problems of stress and depression and underlines the importance of employers introducing carefully considered mental health policies which are cost-effective and meet actual need.

The Health and Safety Commission which I chair and its executive arm, the Health and Safety Executive (HSE), have long recognised the need for a positive approach to mental health in the workplace. HSE has published guidance for employers on identifying and tackling mental health problems among their workforces. It has also sponsored research into a wide range of issues relating to occupational stress and other forms of mental illness at work.

More remains to be done, however, both to promote good practice and guide employers seeking to develop policies on mental health in the workplace. This publication contributes to this process. It is a compendium of both knowledge and experience and will, I believe, prove a useful vehicle for extending understanding and promoting further improvements in the management and prevention of mental ill-health in the workplace. I warmly commend it to you.

Foreword by Michael Bett, Deputy Chairman, British Telecom and President Elect, Institute of Personnel Management

In my roles as Deputy Chairman of British Telecom, and President Elect of IPM, I have become convinced of the importance to British Industry of promoting mental health in the workplace. We are all now agreed on the necessity for workplace policies on such topics as alcohol, drugs, AIDS and accident prevention. However, the burden of mental health problems in the workplace far exceeds all these other topics put together. I believe the time is ripe to face this challenge.

In order to do so, it will be necessary to combat the stigma attached to mental health issues which, so often, conspires to prevent adequate discussion and planning. This process has already begun. The heavy media coverage given to this conference, and the issues it raised, attest to the fact that there is considerable public support for taking action in this area.

The evidence presented in this conference make it clear that it is in employers' best interests to pay attention to the mental health of their workforce. Regardless of the causes of mental ill health, the consequences are costly to employers. Only by promoting mental health, by developing systems for prompt detection and management of common conditions such as depression and anxiety, and by developing a framework for the successful rehabilitation back to work of those with severer illnesses after a prolonged absence, can employers hope to minimise these costs and reap the rewards of a healthy workforce. These considerations are even more vital in a time of economic difficulty, when the productivity and commitment of the workforce is critical.

In my period as President of IPM, this is one of the priorities I shall be pursuing with my fellow industralists.

Introduction

Virginia Bottomley

Six million people in the UK suffer from mental illness each year. It is as common as heart disease, and three times as common as cancer. It is a huge burden of illness in society and yet, because so much stigma still attaches to mental illness, it is the one topic that we are still scared to think and talk about. It is also responsible for a significant number of deaths. Each year in England, 5½ thousand people kill themselves. This is as high as deaths from road traffic accidents and is a major avoidable mortality.

You may say, 'What has this to do with us'? The answer is that no workforce is exempt. A company of 1000 employees can expect between 200 and 300 people with with depression and anxiety in a year and 1 suicide every decade. Each year in this country, 8 million working days are lost through alcohol and drink related disease, 35 million through coronary heart disease and stroke, and 80 million through mental illness. And this figure is a minimum estimate because many people are reluctant to let their employers know that they have been depressed or otherwise mentally ill. And GPs often fail to recognise depression, or to recognise that physical symptoms can be emotional in origin.

Individuals, families, their friends and work colleagues all suffer when someone becomes mentally ill. By far the commonest forms of mental illness are depression and anxiety. With their accompanying symptoms of fatigue, poor concentration and irritability, depression and anxiety may cause problems, not just at home with the family, but also in the workplace, leading to increased sickness absence, increased labour turnover, lowered performance, poor relationships with colleagues and even to accidents. The financial cost of mental illness to industry has been estimated at over £3.7 billion a year. Treating mental illness costs the NHS some £2 billion a year, some 20% of the total bill. And this does not include the cost to local authority social services. So it makes both human and economic sense to devote effort to tackling mental illness in our society.

The working environment is also an important source of support, providing social interaction, personal identity, a sense of purpose, variety and interest. Effective health policies at work can make an important contribution to the prevention and management of mental health problems.

This conference is about bringing together an alliance of organisations and interested employers, personnel managers, health and safety representatives and health professionals to discuss the business case for adopting mental health policies, including the prevention of stress, depression and anxiety, and their prompt detection and management. It is the second in our series on mental health in the workplace. The first was held in collaboration with the CBI and was opened by my predecessor, William Waldegrave, just over a year ago.

In the short space of time since then we have achieved a great deal. Last summer saw the Launch of the 'Health of the Nation' White Paper which sets out clear health objectives and targets against which to monitor progress. We have identified five key areas where improvements can be made, and these are coronary heart disease and stroke, cancers, mental illness, sexual health and accidents.

We have also defined a number of contexts where action is planned to achieve the targets, including local communities, schools, the workplace and the National Health Service. The workplace is one of the most important settings in the achievement of health gain. For 25 million people in the country the greater part of their working lives is spent at work. The workplace provides a unique opportunity to deliver health education messages and promote healthy behaviour.

The one way in which most, if not all, of the population can be reached is by concerted, combined action – by the formation of what we call 'healthy alliances'. One of the main themes of the White Paper is the recognition of the central role of such alliances.

Our Wider Health Group, chaired by Minister of Health Dr Brian Mawhinney, has been given a specific remit to prepare and consult on guidance about healthy alliances. Alliances are necessary at all levels: at National level between Government Departments and national agencies, and at local level between health authorities, employers, local authorities and voluntary bodies.

Some alliances already exist – the CBI and TUC have both supported the National 'Look after Your Heart' programme run jointly by my Department and the Health Education Authority, with the result that its workplace initiative now covers over 700 employers and nearly 4 million employees, but there is room for many more alliances.

A new alliance which was recently brought to my attention is that between MIND and COHSE, the Health Care Union, who have collaborated to produce an excellent set of Guidelines for Empowering Users of Mental Health Services. The guidelines were prepared in response to a straightforward desire by COHSE members to respond positively to the self advocacy movement of users of mental health services, and with the belief that the empowerment of receipients of mental health services goes hand in hand with campaigns for better working conditions. Both are part of the general movement towards equality and human rights.

MIND has also recently produced an Action Pack on Mental Health and Employment – A Guide to good practice, which includes briefing on good practice in the workplace, a model of practice on recruitment and selection of people with a previous history of mental illness, and a useful resource list. Clearly it is for employers to build closer partnerships with the voluntary bodies and local and central government agencies. These can offer sources of advice and practical help on what employers can do to help their own people overcome mental health problems. Good links, formal or otherwise, between employers, local authorities and social services, voluntary bodies such as MIND and Government agencies are of great value.

This conference, which marks the European Year of Health and Safety, is a healthy alliance and historic collaboration between the Department of Health, the Institute of Personnel Managers, the CBI, the TUC, the Health and Safety Executive, the Department of Employment, the Health Education Authority and the Advisory and Concilitation Service in order to present a programme to you today on the business case for adopting mental health policies in the workplace.

The idea of promoting health at work is of course not new, and several companies which have taken steps in this direction are represented here today. I would also like to take this opportunity of warmly welcoming the Wellness Forum's initiative. This Forum, mainly of employers, has brought together like minded individuals with a common aim of developing the Wellness of their employees through prevention.

As part of the implementation of the 'Health of the Nation', and complementary to the Wellness initiative, a Task Force has been set up to develop healthy workplaces. The Task Force is chaired by Terry Hogg, Director of Production at Nissan UK, and it will be looking at opportunities across all five of the Health of the Nation key areas. I would urge everyone to support it in carrying out its work – in identifying what approaches work best, how larger companies might assist the introduction of health education into smaller workplaces, and demonstrating the cost effectiveness of health education.

As a major employer, the NHS is taking action to improve the health of its own workforce. The Chief Executive is initiating and personally overseeing systematic work within the NHS, to test some very concrete ideas for organising work at hospital level, of which one consequence should be a reduction in absence due to mental ill health.

We are keen to encourage research in this area, and the 'Mental health of the NHS workforce' has been selected as one of our six national research priorities in mental health. We are about to commission a body of studies in this field examining prevalence of mental health problems and methods of prevention. Our workforce is so enormous and varied, that the results will also have some general applicability.

In my own Department, we take the responsibility of promoting health education very seriously indeed and regard it as being of paramount importance. For example, it was the first Government Department to sign up to the Look after Your Heart Programme (a Programme, as I am sure you will know, to reduce the incidence of coronary heart disease) Earlier this year a Health Week was organised, the aims of which were not just to raise awareness about the benefits of leading healthy lifestyles but also on other health issues of concern such as asthma, diabetes, sickle cell anaemia, back pain and HIV/AIDS.

I am sure you will agree that it is essential that health promotion activities are targeted properly if they are to have an effect. There is a need therefore, for organisations to have a comprehensive strategy for health promotion within the workplace. My own Department is at present drawing up such a strategy, which has as its basis Health of the Nation. It will therefore focus on the five key areas: coronary heart disease, cancers, mental illness, HIV/ AIDS and sexual health and accidents. The strategy will be reviewed annually to ensure that it continues to be dynamic and relevant. From the strategy will evolve a work programme for the year ahead.

You may be interested to know that we have issued the following policy statements to members of staff:

* sensible drinking which gives line managers advice on handling problem drinkers and sources of help
* drug misuse – this gives advice again to line managers on how to identify and help any member of staff who is misusing drugs and stresses that drug misuse should be seen as a form of illness and that drug misusers should be encouraged to seek treatment.

* HIV/AIDS – the policy statement gives information about the transmission of HIV to allay fears about transmission and stresses the need to take all reasonable measures to ensure that internal or external applicants for vacancies are not discriminated against on the grounds they are HIV positive.

* Our Mental illness policy statement is currently being drawn up. It will set out the action which should be taken to help members of staff with mental health problems. The aims of the policy will be to provide information to staff on the causes and effects of mental illness; to encourage and to assist members of staff with mental health problems to seek help at an early stage and to advise line managers on how they can assist a member of staff with a mental health problem.

'Healthy workplaces' can benefit individuals and organisations; your employees, your businesses and yourselves. We can ill afford an unhealthy workforce. As a sign of our commitment to this issue, occupational mental health features in my report on Mental Illness Services laid before Parliament last month. This report gives an account of main developments over the last year. My presence here this morning demonstrates my concern 'to raise employers' awareness of this important subject and to encourage the development of corporate mental health policies which address primary, secondary and tertiary prevention of mental health problems in the workplace'.*

That is why I am delighted to be here this morning to welcome you to our second Department of Health Conference on Mental Health in the Workplace and to talk about our strategy for improving health. Your active help and participation as employers, line managers, personnel officers, occupational health professionals and health and safety officers will be vital to achieving our health goals. And progress in creating a healthy workforce will in turn have great benefits for Industry in terms of higher morale, reduced absenteeism, reduced staff turnover and greater effectiveness. I look forward to working with you to achieve better health.

---

* Disabled Persons (Services, Consultation and Representation) Act 1986
Development of Services for People with Learning Disabilities (Mental Handicap) or Mental Illness in England.
Fourth Report prepared pursuant to Section 11 of the Disabled Persons (Services, Consultation and Representation) Act 1986. Ordered by the House of Commons to be printed 16 December 1992 London HMSO.

1

THE BUSINESS CASE: CBI's VIEW

Howard Davies

Mental health may appear an unusual subject for the CBI, or indeed the TUC. It appears to have very little to do with the recession, interest rates or economic forecasts, my routine concerns. Some people may also question whether this is a matter for employers at all, or whether the mental health of individuals should only involve those individuals and their medical advisers. I don't accept that argument, though of course I understand the need for clinical confidentiality. Employers can generate stress; they can also help to alleviate it. If this conference does nothing else, I hope it will demonstrate that employers must take an interest in this issue. It is in their interests to do so. We at the CBI are convinced that the mental health of a company's employees can have an important impact on business performance in the same way as does a poor industrial relations climate or inadequate training. That is why the CBI continues to add its voice to the campaign to raise the profile of mental health as a workplace issue.

Mental ill-health, such as stress, anxiety or depression, is still very often perceived as a problem which affects only an unfortunate few, and which is very unlikely to affect anyone in employment. Again, I hope that today will demonstrate that that is a myth. Later this morning you will be hearing about the incidence of mental ill-health amongst the working population.

A central message for industry is that mental ill-health is indiscriminate: there is no immunity granted by position, age or sex. So the potential implications for a company are considerable.

And not just companies. On the proportions suggested by Mrs Bottomley at least four members of cabinet are likely to be depressed and anxious. I can think of a good dozen who have every reason to be!

A CBI/Department of Health survey of CBI members carried out in 1991 showed that employers estimate that approximately 30% of their employees' sick leave is related to stress, anxiety or depression. With the Health and Safety Executive estimating that working days lost due to mental illness are costing employers between one and two billion pounds, with additional costs from poor performance from those who continue to work while mentally ill in some way, the scale of the problem is immense. Of course no action by management will remove the problem entirely, but early identification, and good counselling, can help to head off many emerging problems.

The same 1991 survey also showed that 95% of the respondents considered that the mental health of their employees should be of concern to their company. On the other hand, only 13% of those actually had a company policy or programme in place relating to the promotion of employees' mental health. There may, of course, be a number of companies which did not recognise that the action they are taking could be considered a policy or programme, and so that 13% is likely to hide some very worthwhile work. But the figures clearly point to a gap which needs to be filled if business performance is to be improved.

Whether an individual's stress is work-induced or not, the symptoms in the workplace can have a devastating effect. Increased sickness absence (physical or not), lack of concentration, low morale and poor interpersonal skills are just a few of the indicators that an employee may not be coping. These are signs that no business can afford to ignore, particularly in the current economic climate when the contribution of every employee is crucial if the company is to survive.

It is because of these effects that every reasonable step that can be taken by the employer to reduce the work-induced stress should be considered very carefully. For example, job design and individual discretion over tasks; training to cope with new technology; communication, particularly in times of change: these are only a few of the areas where improvements can reap substantial rewards. A number of companies are also recognising the benefits to be gained from counselling schemes and Employee Assistance Programmes, of which I am sure you will hear more throughout today. For example, The Post Office and Whitbread both have successful, though very different, counselling programmes. I understand you will also hear today from Marks and Spencer about their very comprehensive health programme.

Good communication is critical. We know, for example, that an important cause of stress is fear of unemployment. A recent survey showed that some four million employees feared they might lose their job in the next year. On the most pessimistic forecast, three and a half million of them are concerned unnecessarily. Some of that needless anxiety could be removed by better communication. It must, however, be recognised that not all stress-inducers are controllable by the employer. Marital or family problems, bereavement, financial problems, and moving house are some of the other common sources of stress which can also have marked effects on an individual's work performance. In such situations, the workplace can try to be a positive influence, but its ability to solve the problem is somewhat limited.

This principle of exerting a positive workplace influence goes well beyond mental health, and is followed by many companies for a variety of health issues. The Secretary of State's 'Health of the Nation' White Paper has adopted this principle and so is raising the profile not only of mental illness, but also of many other health issues, as workplace concerns.

The CBI supports the educative, informative and advisory role that the White Paper suggests industry can fulfil in meeting the Government's health targets. I am sure that this will create extensive debate on the role of the employer in influencing employees' lifestyles. Different companies have very different views about how far into an employee's lifestyle they can tread, for example on smoking and drinking habits.

To assist us in representing the business view on wider occupational health issues such as these, I am pleased to announce that we will be carrying out a survey of our members. This will ascertain the extent of provision by employers on a number of health issues, such as HIV/AIDS, mental health, drugs, alcohol, and health screening. In particular, we will examine the views of CBI members on their role in the health of their employees; whether they see that role as limited to meeting legal requirements, to protect against particular risks, or more broadly to improve their employees' fitness for work. Whilst not promising a comprehensive answer to the problem of defining the employer role, I hope that this survey will give an insight into the health philosophies of CBI member companies. We intend to publish the results later this year.

In conclusion, I would like to reiterate CBI's commitment to mental health as a business concern, and our determination to encourage more organisations to follow the lead given by the companies speaking today. It has proved beneficial for them to spend the time, energy and resources on this issue, and can, I hope, only act as a stimulus to other companies, large and small.

I hope I have convinced you of the reasons why business cannot afford to ignore this issue. I would have liked to be able to highlight more concrete examples of the benefits to be reaped from action on mental health, but unfortunately information on effectiveness is rather sparse. I am sure that industry would welcome more work in this area, assisting them in evaluating and decision making. That may flow from this conference, and from the Department's own activities.

The Business Case: TUC's View

Alan Tuffin

Mental Health At Work
Royal College of Physicians: January 11, 1993

My thanks to the Royal College of Physicians for this opportunity to address you this morning at what I believe is an important and timely conference. I wish to confine my comments primarily to the issue of stress at the workplace.

Many people are subjected to stress both in work and in society. Low paid workers are often in jobs which are less secure and they have to cope with the stresses of poor standards of living. In particular single parents and women with a dual role, with responsibilities in employment and for dependants, are often in low paid, part-time, low graded jobs. The TUC has policies aimed at reducing some of these causes of stress such as poverty, poor housing and unemployment. Trade unions are also active in seeking to assist members whose personal circumstances present additional pressures for them in work. Such help may be the provision of details of the sources of professional counselling and support; negotiating more flexible working hours and special leave; and the negotiation of workplace nurseries.

Recognised trade union safety representatives are able to represent and put right many aspects of jobs and the way in which work is organised which can create stress and ill health. It is now known that, when the level of stress is continuous and becomes unmanageable, ill health will be the result. Therefore, trade unions have set about (1) investigating what it is that creates unacceptable levels of stress and (2) identifying the changes which employers should make to reduce the risks to the health of their employees.

It is often difficult for safety representatives to get the problem of stress taken seriously by employers. This is partly due to the fact that the effects of stress will vary from one person to another and the level of stress may be difficult to measure. More often employers, if they recognise it at all, will see signs of stress as an individual rather than an employment problem.

Definition of Stress

Stress is something to which we are all subjected and our understanding of it is far from complete. It is a word which is often used to describe fatigue and a feeling of not being able to cope. Others see it as a driving force which helps them to survive more effectively. People respond to the same situation in very different ways. Some will find a repetitive job comfortable, others frustrating because it provides no challenge. Some will manage a stressful situation for a period of time and then find it intolerable.

Also while it is possible to identify physical causes of stress, such as noise and temperature levels, it is much more difficult to identify workload and conflict levels. Stress will result if the demands made on the individual do not match the resources available [in the person or provided by the organisation] or do not meet the individual's needs and motivation. For example, stress will be the result if the workload is too large for the number of workers and the time available. Equally, a boring repetitive task which does not use the potential skills and experience of some individuals will also cause stress.

What is it about work that causes stress?

Insecurity

For many workers one of the major causes of stress is rising insecurity and fear of unemployment. The threat of redundancies may be real, or used to put pressure on the workforce and weaken trade union organisation. This seems to me to be a more relevant issue in today's economic circumstances than a number of years ago.

The pressure of job insecurity linked to that of low pay and career loss – especially affecting the low paid who are first to be made redundant – are high on the list of causes.

Insecurity can also occur if people do not feel confident about their ability to do the job well and do not have enough time, information, training or support to do the job. If they lack confidence that support will be forthcoming where mistakes are made and disciplinary procedures are rigidly applied, this too will increase individuals' feelings of insecurity. Also people will feel at risk where changes in the organisation, jobs, equipment, layout and style of supervision occur with little consultation or information about the changes being made or without any training in new methods or equipment.

However, in workplaces where unions are organised, membership does give individual workers means of influencing what happens to them in their working lives. Trade unions seek, through negotiation, to influence management decisions about such things as re-structuring, training and job security. Trade union membership also means that individuals know they have available representation and protection in cases of unfair discipline, unfair dismissal or if they have special problems at their place of work.

Long Hours

Long hours and low pay often go together to cause stress. Overtime can lead to disruption of family and social life and fatigue, and can increase accident risks.

Shiftwork

Workers on 'twilight' or night shifts face stress problems on top of those faced by other workers. The most obvious is the social cost of working when family and friends are at home. Single parent and women working shifts will often have to cope with domestic responsibilities as well as the need to earn a living. Many shiftworkers are at risk from:

disturbed and inadequate sleep patterns;

consequential fatigue;

depression and neuroses.

Lack of Job Satisfaction and Control

This is one of the most important areas of occupational stress – and one of the slowest to improve. Many workers are at risk from boring monotonous or over-demanding jobs. The control of occupational stress must start from the recognition that the main changes must be in design of jobs, the way work is organised and in ensuring well designed workplaces.

On the physical effects of stress, I will leave this to our later speakers – except to say that illnesses associated with mental strain are not usually classified as 'occupational diseases'. Few records are kept, even though the origins of stress related ill health may be clear to the millions of workers who are suffering every day.

Mental strain or mental ill health caused by stress in work is very rarely examined. Society's attitudes to mental ill-health are very different from those to physical ill health. The stigma can add to pressure on the stressed individual and may cause them to try and hide the effects until they become so great that the symptoms are unavoidable. The use of emotive terms such as 'breakdown' and 'burnout' do not help stressed people.

TUC Activity and Concerns

The TUC and affiliated unions have devoted increasing attention to raising awareness of stress at work as a major source of occupationally related health damage, affecting both the mental and physical well-being of workers. In common with many other sources of work-related health risk, developing effective approaches to control of occupational stress has been complicated by the fact that non-occupational sources of stress are widespread, and there is a wide range of response amongst individuals to the same sources of stress in the work setting. The general objective of the TUC and unions however, has been to focus on those aspects of the job which their members do and the way in which work is organised which can create stress and lead to ill health.

While there are wide variations in individual response to occupational stress, the TUC has sought to raise awareness of the issue as a collective rather than an individual problem. In its guidance on stress in the TUC's health and safety guide 'Hazards at Work' the TUC has focused on four sources of stress: environment; job design; contractual issues; and working relationships. The guidance aims to assist readers to develop an assessment of these factors, including an assessment of stress effects amongst members, and to develop approaches to control.

The TUC is continuing informal discussions with MIND and the CBI in the light of the recent CBI Conference on Mental Health. Contact is also being maintained with the Department of Employment initiatives. The International Labour Organisation [ILO] is at present working on a handbook of case studies on reducing and managing stress in industrial occupations.

The new duties on employers to consult unions about the health and safety consequences of changes in the workplace will mean in practice that guidance will be needed to develop effective approaches to assessment of the impact of changes in work systems, for example approaches to the detailed analysis of tasks.

The TUC has established a Common Action Priority Team on Stress which, in addition to trade union experts in this field includes occupational psychologists. This team will carry out a mapping exercise leading to recommendations on particular initiatives that could be pursued by the TUC and unions. The Team begins its work shortly.

I have spoken about the effects that work can have on the mental health of employees but we should also be considering the place of work in the lives of people with diagnosed mental illness.

Many employers now claim to be equal opportunity employers but discussion of how to accept people with mental illness into the workplace is still taboo. In addition to work by employers trade unions too have a job of education to carry out with their members.

The TUC has expressed it criticisms at the failure of government to properly resource continuing and added responsibilities of Community Care when people with mental illness are now being released from hospital into the community. This was tragically exemplified by the recent incident at London Zoo.

I am not suggesting that the workplace becomes a treatment centre but the workplace and the people that work there are part of the community. One person in ten, at some stage in their life, will be afflicted by mental illness. Not only that individual is affected but also that person's family, friends and workmates.

I trust that today's timely conference is a success and that we will come away from today's discussion clearer in our ability to recognise stress, to deal with symptoms , to locate and remove the source and to look at mental ill-health in a positive way.

3

The Business Case
Action taken by ICI – Zeneca

Barrie Thorpe and Eric Teasdale

Introduction

On 1 January 1993, ICI's Pharmaceuticals business together with the Agrochemicals and Seeds and Specialties Businesses became the constituent members of Zeneca Limited – this is a wholly owned subsidiary of ICI PLC. 'New' ICI consists of the other international businesses, namely Paints, Industrial Chemicals, Materials, Explosives and Tioxide Ltd.

Zeneca Pharmaceuticals is a large organisation and the reader may benefit from hearing something of the dimensions, characteristics and 'mission' statement of this business. This will allow the activities described to be put in context.

In terms of **DIMENSIONS** the Business, in 1991, had a turnover of £1.6 billion sterling and sold its products in 130 countries. Manufacturing takes place in 17 countries and 13,000 people are involved in the total operations. Research and development 'spend' amounted to £220 million per annum which is approximately 14% of sales.

Products which have recently been launched include 'Zestril' (a medicine used for cardiovascular conditions), 'Diprivan' (an anaesthetic) and 'Zoladex' (an anti-cancer agent). There is an exciting new product development pipeline which includes 'Merrem' (an antibiotic), 'Casodex' (an anti-cancer agent) and 'Accolate' (a novel therapy for asthma).

In terms of **GEOGRAPHIC SPREAD**, of the 13,000 employed in the Business 4,400 work in the UK, 3,500 in Continental Western Europe, 2,800 in USA, 800 in Japan and 1,500 in territories located in the rest of the world. By function, 4,700 are involved in Sales and Marketing, 3,600 in Manufacturing, 3,300 in Research and Development and 1,400 in Administration.

The Pharmaceuticals industry is an extremely competitive sector in which to operate and is exposed to pressures which can translate themselves into high levels of stress in individuals. It is also largely research orientated, depending on a high degree of creativity with long periods of uncertainty as to the final outcome of expensive development programmes. Such factors compound the pressure on individuals. Tight control of costs, a high volume of new work, the drive for high quality and compliance with Regulatory Authority requirements and the law all make the working environment tough and demanding.

It is essential for any organisation to define clearly the main areas of activity and thereby target resources appropriately. The 'Mission' of Zeneca Pharmaceuticals is 'To contribute to human health by providing worthwhile products which enable the business to grow and the people in it to prosper and lead fulfilling lives'.

An enormous amount of work is going into research and development of new medicines and the current objective is to bring one new product through to launch each year. To achieve this and to ensure that the established business thrives, it is essential to have a 'healthy' organisation. This implies having healthy people who are motivated and clearly focussed on the job in hand. Ultimately the success of the business depends on the people in it.

Health and Stress

What is HEALTH? It has been defined in many ways. Amongst them are:

> *'a state of complete physical, mental and social well-being, not merely the absence of disease or infirmity'.*

> *' . . . a personal experience of positive enjoyment of life'.*

In the occupational or industrial setting, the emphasis on maintaining **mental** (as well as physical and social) well-being is essential to success. In extreme cases mental illness must be recognised and managed appropriately. This should include the care of the individual who has a problem of substance abuse eg alcohol or drugs of addiction, and the patient with a psychotic condition where prompt admission to hospital is required. In practice, however, the more common mental health problems encompass stress, anxiety and depression and their manifestation in the workplace.

It is estimated that 1.5 million working days are lost in the UK each year through stress related illness. Any initiative to remedy this is to be welcomed. In addition to lost time, if employees are under excessive and prolonged pressure for too long, this can lead to an increased incidence of unsafe working practices and accidents in the workplace. There can also be a loss of 'creative edge'. Poor performance and low morale may also result. Most organisations may provide no more than a casualty service involving nurses and/or occupational physicians who recognise casualties and deal with them appropriately. It is, we believe, essential to have a positive strategy to manage stress, make it a subject for legitimate discussion and recognise stress-related conditions as having the potential for disrupting efficiency and productivity.

Managing health should be recognised as a 'line management' accountability. Managers should manage people as well as tasks, plant and projects. Obviously close liaison with the occupational health and personnel functions is likely to be required.

Any problem can best be handled if it is possible to measure the extent of the situation or the number of people affected. In other words, **if you want to 'manage' then being able to 'measure' is essential**. Dealing with problems which individuals encounter must be handled with sensitivity. Confidentiality must be protected. There will be occasions where the manager is unaware of the difficulties being experienced by specific individuals but senior managers must understand the overall picture.

Self awareness and self management must be promoted – the individual should be encouraged to learn skills and be aware of how he or she copes with increasing demands placed on them.

What is 'STRESS'? One observer described it as 'a reality like love or electricity – unmistakable in experience but hard to define'. Stress is, of course, not confined to the workplace but may be related to homelife and the social scene. '**OCCU-PATIONAL STRESS**' can mean either the pressure that work puts on individuals or the effect of that pressure. All work puts some pressure on individuals; in general the more demanding the work the greater the stress. This normally leads to higher output and satisfaction with work. However a point of diminishing returns is reached beyond which increasing stress leads to reversed effects; lowered efficiency, job satisfaction, performance and mental well-being (Cooper and Marshall, 1980). **Stress itself is not an illness; rather it is a state. However, it is a very powerful cause of illness. Long term excessive stress is known to lead to serious health problems**.

There is a bewildering array of books, magazine articles, television programmes and training courses about stress. Some of these can help you find out what stress is, but they rarely give you much of an idea what you can do about it. Stress is best thought of as a series of physical and mental reflexes which exist because they have had a purpose. They are designed to put your body and mind into overdrive for short periods of time, and to help your system to deal with short-term crises. It is presumably because they have a survival value that they have been bred into us in times long gone – the fastest runners and the hardest fighters were the ones who survived.

The problem for us in the modern world is that few of the pressures on us which produce stress, so called 'stressors', can be dealt with by direct physical action – no matter how much we might be tempted by the idea. The aim of quickly getting rid of the stress is usually hard to achieve. As a result we are left with the physical and mental effects over periods of weeks, months or even years since the stressors that we have to deal with do not go away.

Many people feel that experiencing unpleasant stress is a weakness or that they should be able to use their mind or their logic to switch stress off. That is unrealistic; most of us have had the experience of feeling jittery after a near miss in the car, even though we know that the threat has passed and we are completely safe. The stress responses are a set of automatic reflexes which are there to protect us and cannot be switched off.

Fig 1 depicts the relationship between stress, or pressure/demands on the individual (along the horizontal axis), and performance or output (the vertical axis).

This relationship can be demonstrated both at an individual level and at an organisational level. For example, at the individual level the physical responses to stress (eg the changes which can be observed in breathing rate and blood pressure) and psychological performance (eg performing mental arithmetic under time pres-

Figure 1

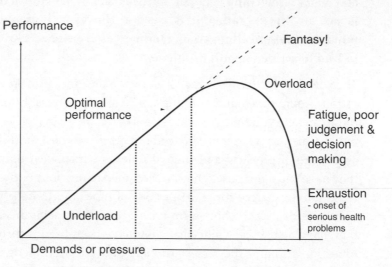

sures). At the organisational level it is apparent in terms of group performance such as the productivity or efficiency levels.

Note that initially performance improves under pressure; this is why athletes often produce better results when competing than they do in practice sessions. The whole science of training and sports coaching is aimed at building competitors up to optimal performance for the day of the big event. However, this improvement does not go on forever. There comes a point where performance begins to deteriorate – an experience that all of us will have recognised in others, if not in ourselves. If the pressure is not reduced, then performance is sub-optimal and may even lead to break-down.

We all perform at our best when under the right amount of pressure. There comes a point when the pressure becomes too much and our performance suffers. It is important to be aware of the consequences and notice when our efficiency is begin-ning to fall off. Most people are bad at monitoring their own stress levels but better at seeing it in colleagues or in friends and family. Brief overload does nothing more than temporarily reduce performance; major overload can produce serious prob-lems. **Stress, of course, is a normal part of life. The challenge is to manage the pressures so that life is productive and enjoyable**.

The ICI/Zeneca Approach

HISTORY. In the mid 1980s, the number of cases of stress related illness in ICI Pharmaceuticals reported to the Occupational Health Department indicated a disturbing upward trend. It may be of interest to display three case histories which demonstrate how stress related problems can be manifested.

Mr A has to co-ordinate the submission of the information to obtain a product licence for a new compound. He works night and day – co-ordinating the efforts of people from individual departments. He has been told– 'the business depends on you'. His free time shrinks, his wife and family get the rough edge of his tongue over many months, he feels unsupported at work and unable to say that he can't cope. At 9pm after a train journey from London he bursts into tears on the station platform. Six months later he still lacks confidence but is learning to work more effectively and still find time for himself and his family.

Mrs B is engaged in a number of negotiations with other companies. New projects and negotiations are initiated regularly and require concentration over long hours. The projects require managing – she plays a key role in supporting and advancing each one. Work starts at 8am and never seems to stop. Holidays and weekends don't exist. Hobbies are a thing of the past. She wishes manpower requirements to manage new projects were planned at the outset. On two occasions she has been seen leaving her office at 7pm. Eventually she is taken off her job for two weeks rest. Mrs B is lucky – her overwork was recognised as such and she is not considered to have failed. Others are branded as 'weak'.

Mr C is promoted to senior staff level. He is well trained and capable. He works hard but is unable to prioritise his tasks and give each one full attention. No one asks him to outline his workload and allocate appropriate time to each task. He works 10 or 11 hours daily and is usually busy with work at weekends. The initial enthusiasm at the promotion is replaced by anxiety. He feels desperate, panic stricken and becomes depressed. One month's intensive treatment as an outpatient restores his health, vigour and enthusiasm. He needs training in managing his time. His manager needs to not only delegate the authority to look after various aspects of the departmental workload but share some of the responsibility for completion – within appropriate timescales.

Senior members of the occupational health and personnel functions met in late 1987 and a paper was drafted for presentation to the Chairman and Board of Directors of the Business. Within that paper, the likely reasons for the increase in the number of stress cases within the Pharmaceuticals business were highlighted. This list is probably applicable to many other organisations.

1. Rapid growth.

2. Increasing complexity.

3. Organisational change to meet growth.

4. Drive to become truly 'international'.

5. Pressure to sustain a high level of profit.

6. Pressure to bring new products to the market.

7. Tight control of manpower.

8. Sheer volume of new work.

9. High quality of work expected.

10. Commitment reaching level where guilt is felt whenever work is not being done.

11. Difficulty in matching people to jobs.

12. The volume of paper.

It was acknowledged that many of the people who get to the more senior jobs are relatively tough and resilient. For that reason, they may find it hard to understand why some of their subordinates find difficulty in coping. Stress may, however, affect individuals at *all* levels. The Board was asked, using the management system, to acknowledge the legitimacy of the concern and the proposals they were supporting to respond to it. The Board committed itself to a number of specific actions:

1. Encouraging staff to ensure that they dealt with essential tasks and were selective in use of time.

2. Continuing a number of existing training activities eg 'Time-Management' and 'Management of Change' courses.

3. A one-day workshop to be established on the topic of stress.

4. Guidance to be given on travel schedules, planning meetings etc.

5. Medical screening to include assessment of mental health – and guidance to be given to those requiring assistance.

6. The match between people and jobs to be a priority. The personnel function to support this by continuing to improve selection and assessment techniques.

7. The annual appraisal mechanism to be used to review workload and draft individual development plans, such that staff are given the opportunity to develop skills and acquire knowledge to match the demands of the job.

8. Managers to manage *people* as well as tasks and projects. They are in the ideal situation to help and support their staff. As individuals may, however, choose to seek the assistance of a counsellor outwith their normal sphere, the Personnel and Occupational Health functions should have sufficient trained people to meet this need. These counsellors must know when it is essential to refer individuals for more skilled or specialist support.

THE CEO's LETTER – If stress management is to be effective, it must percolate into the culture of the organisation rather than be limited to the agenda of a few training sessions. A pivotal step was the distribution to all departmental heads of a letter signed by the CEO. This reads as follows:

'I know that in recent months a number of Managers and employees have been concerned about the increasing demands of the business on employees and have seen this exemplified in a small but significant number of employees with serious problems.

The business will continue to expand and it is important that appropriate pressure is placed on staff. Some stress is good for both individuals and the business leading to job satisfaction, motivation and good performance. Too much or inappropriate pressure on people who are unable to cope with it is bad for them and bad for the business.

It is important for Managers to keep under surveillance the total workload on individuals and groups making sure that priorities and reasonable timescales are set. For example, I see it as important that staff have enough free time for outside pursuits. If work takes up more than a reasonable proportion of an individual's time, over too long a period, the business is unlikely to benefit in the long term. In this context an individual's holiday arrangements should only rarely be disrupted. The sensible planning and allocation of work within your departments is a vital factor in maximising efficiency. I would ask you to pay particular attention to staff whose duties oblige them to do a lot of travelling, and ensure that they plan their schedules in a sensible way.

I have asked the Personnel and Occupational Health departments to pursue with you a number of detailed proposals designed to ensure a fuller appreciation of these issues and to minimise the incidence of stress related problems in the organisation.'

This letter led to a great deal of 'behind the scenes' discussion and support; not surprisingly some senior managers were threatened by the idea of employees apparently being told to work less hard and to consider their family and social lives as a high priority. In some quarters there was genuine fear that the commercial momentum of the organisation might be impaired. It will come as no surprise to those involved in organisational development work that this was not the case and indeed it seems likely that the reverse effect occurred. There is every indication that commitment and efficiency have improved. There is no doubt, however, that this letter and the known existence of high level working parties, increased interest and underlined credibility to all staff.

STRESS MANAGEMENT WORKSHOPS – agreement was reached that four pilot stress management workshops would be held, organised and presented by the Training Section of Personnel department and Occupational Health jointly. The objectives for the workshops were set as follows:

1. To raise awareness of what is meant by 'Stress'.

2. To legitimise Stress as a subject for discussion in the Business.

3. To show a range of Stress Management skills with a view to further skills training.

4. To practice two key Stress Managament skills ie listening and relaxation.

The workshops started in January 1988 and by the beginning of 1993 almost 700 individuals had attended. It was a deliberate policy to start at the top and work outwards – the first three workshops were attended by most of the Directors of the business.

The idea behind the stress management workshop is relatively straightforward. It is to show people that stress is a normal part of a healthy life which can, however, get out of control. It is important therefore to be able to recognise – in oneself and others – when stress levels are becoming too great, and to do something about it before 'overload' is reached; that is, to learn 'stress management' skills. **The workshop is not intended to be a counselling forum for people who are deemed to have stress related problems**. The workshop is spread over 1 full day with a follow up $\frac{1}{2}$ day one month later. The organisers point out that participation in any workshop activity is voluntary and that all discussions are strictly confidential. As with most successful training programmes, the workshop involves a great deal of active participation. The day is relaxed and informal. The first exercise is simple and deceptively effective. Privately and in pairs, each participant spends 5 minutes telling their partner the sources of stress in their lives. One person talks the other listens. Roles are then reversed.

Back at base, everyone is asked in turn to describe what if any value such an exercise had but *not* to reveal the details. What emerges is surprisingly uniform; that there is a large degree of empathy – what stresses one person more often than not also stresses the other; and that simply to have someone who is patiently listening to you, and showing genuine interest in what you are saying, is in itself of immense value. Already, one hour into the day one of the big barriers to success from stress management is crumbling. Stress is not confined to one or two individuals, and it is a legitimate subject for discussion. A group 'brainstorming' session on the general topic of 'what stresses me' enables the course participants to focus more closely on those everyday strains which produce the symptoms of stress. Late trains, cantankerous teenage children, prevaricating estate agents.

A specially commissioned video chronicles the events leading up to the nervous breakdown of John, a (fictitious) 'hard-pressed' ICI employee. In the ensuing discussion the events depicted are picked over with a fine-toothed comb. Why did he take on more work than he could handle? What was the responsibility of his boss? Could the signs have been spotted earlier? A second video shows how a different fictitious employee 'gets it right', and avoids the consequences of his unfortunate colleague. Finally, a brief introduction is given to various techniques of relaxation.

Does the workshop actually do any good? Such things are not easy to measure directly but on the evidence of stress-measurement questionnaires that participants complete before and after the course, stress levels are lowered and the new found skills should help to keep it that way. People are now much more ready to talk about their workload and stress and about what they are doing to cope. The workshops have also helped to identify wider training needs such as 'Assertiveness'. Overall, the number of people presenting with stress related illness is down. Figure 2 displays the number of individuals who needed to be referred to psychiatrists or who attended the ICI Medical Centres or their own family doctor's clinics over the last 10 years.

Figure 2

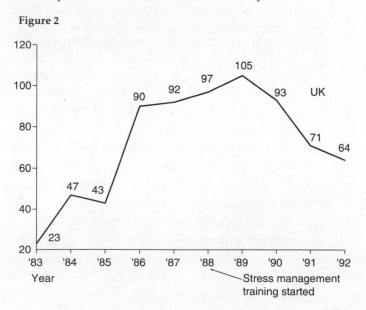

Summary and Conclusions

The challenge is to allow and encourage an appropriate amount of stress or pressure, to enhance the performance of individuals, the departments where they work and thus the Business and Organisation as a whole.

The **ZENECA PHARMACEUTICALS STRATEGY** has been:

1. Early involvement of Directors and General Managers.

2. Collaboration between Occupational Health, Training, Organisational experts and managers.

3. Effective communication with managers regarding the importance of Mental Health and Stress.

4. The introduction of well planned, professional training and educational programmes, including skills training workshops.

5. The evolution of a finely tuned, validated workshop, based around two high quality videos.

6. A complementary counselling and treatment service.

7. Effective publicity with the production of leaflets, booklets and other educational training aids.

8. The development of a cultural change initiative within the Business leading to radical change.

IN SUMMARY: defining objectives and accountability clearly, and setting clear priorities and managing time effectively is essential. In an innovative and demanding environment, maintaining the health of staff and managing stress positively is likely to improve productivity, reduce errors, increase creativity, improve decision making and lead to enhanced job satisfaction.

A policy for Mental Health is not a stand alone initiative, but part of an integrated approach to managing a high quality organisation.

Dr B. J. THORPE BSc PhD
Production Director
ZENECA Pharmaceuticals
Alderley House
Alderley Park
Macclesfield
Cheshire
SK10 4TF

Dr E. L. TEASDALE MBChB
   MRCGP DIH MFOM
Chief Medical Officer
ZENECA Pharmaceuticals
Alderley House
Alderley Park
Macclesfield
Cheshire
SK10 4TF

4

The Business Case – Action taken by Marks & Spencer

Sally Young

Introduction

Marks & Spencer takes the mental health of its workforce extremely seriously, and we realise that in ensuring the mental 'wellbeing' of staff we benefit both from an individual and a company point of view.

The Company – The Facts

I will start by introducing a few key facts that are needed to set in context the issue of mental health at work in a company such as ours.

We are an international retailer with a presence in many areas of the world including North America, The Far East and Europe.

We have 696 stores worldwide, of which 300 are in the UK. 261 are town centre, 27 neighbourhood food and 12 edge-of-town. In the UK we employ 56,000 people, and over 52,000 of these are employed in stores. 83% of the workforce is female and 62% of these are part-time. 14 million people shop weekly in our stores, and last year our turnover was £5 billion.

Company Philosophy

The Company was founded on a philosophy of care for the individual, and this philosophy has been fundamental in enabling us to implement policies that all add up to today's strategy of 'wellness' for our staff.

We have always aimed to develop policies which foster good human relations, fulfilling the needs of the individual, and also responding to the commercial objectives of the Business.

Our overall strategy is moving towards partnership and empowerment through choice, and it is this strategy that you will see reflected in the various exercises described later on. Many of the initiatives could not have been successful if they had not been in the context of such a strategy.

The Company has also sought to maintain a support system within its structure that enables the implementation of general policies affecting the well-being of its major resource. There is a Personnel Management structure which covers each store, and as this moves into the arena of Human Resource Management, so we are developing occupational health teams that enable us to adopt approaches based on prevention and self-help, rather than the traditional methods of treatment and instruction.

The Issue

We have a number of socio-economic factors today that have exacerbated the pressures encountered by individuals, and heightened the issue of managing and balancing the work, individual and environmental pressures encountered by staff.

In the last two years, the most significant of these for us have been:

Company Specific:

- Company re-structuring and re-definition of roles and functions with some redundancies.

- Greater accountability for individuals.

- The further development of IT systems in the workplace.

- Appraisal against targets.

Other Factors:

- Recession.

- Debt and re-possession of property.

- Family redundancies.

- Income reduction.

All of which can have a significant effect on the way in which an individual performs, and can lead to insecurity, anxiety and depression.

Company Responsibility

The fact is that we are living in tough times, and raising the level of performance of your staff will have an obvious benefit to the employer who recognises the need to introduce policies to achieve this. If absence levels alone are reduced, then the Company is benefitting from such action.

In essence, there are three steps to be taken by employers wishing to make improvement in the area of mental health in the workplace:

1. Promote awareness of the issue amongst management and staff. This can take the form of training or provision of support services.

2. Identify a problem-solving mechanism. This is best achieved by a 'bottom up' approach, where the issues are identified and solutions offered by those who are most affected.

3. Implementation of the solutions, and reviews to measure the impact or positive effect of the initiative.

Specific Initiatives

Eight key areas of development are covered:
(a) The development of Occupational Health Teams.
(b) Health through life – education and self-help.
(c) Store-based improvement programmes.
(d) The case for EAP Programmes.
(e) Managing pressure programmes.
(f) The impact of IT.
(g) Secondments and the community.
(h) The Wellness Forum.

The Development of Occupational Health Teams

In moving to a culture today of individualism and partnership, we now use the principle of guided self-help – choice replacing provision, and well-being replacing welfare.

We are wholly committed to the concept of an Occupational Health Service, and work increasingly closely with personnel and line management to create and maintain a framework of health promotion through health education, screening action, and preventative rather then curative clinical services, all of which leaves the individual responsible for making his or her own choice.

In our Head Office, the Occupational Health Team consists of 5 doctors, 3 dentists, oral hygienists and a chiropodist.

We have been piloting the development of occupational health teams in stores, using doctor/nurse teams in two of the six geographical divisions, and are now poised after evaluating the benefits of this approach to extend this policy to the rest of the UK.

There are proven benefits of operating this system and these could be summarised as:

1. Health information becoming more widely available to a greater number of people.

2. The staff in stores being educated to make more informed choices for themselves.

3. What was previously often a re-active service available to a small number has become a pro-active service that is more clearly targeted to the needs of a particular store.

The overall advantages positively affect widely differing spheres of activity including:

- Increasing the level of health education.
- Reducing the number of accidents and the level of absence.
- Counselling provision and problem-solving.
- Better first-aid teams.
- Effective re-habilitation programmes.

Some commercial managers were sceptical in the extreme at the outset, these same managers now see such an advantage commercially to this development that they would not give it up without a hard fight – proof positive of the benefit of the system.

Health Through Life

Marks & Spencer has offered a number of screening programmes to its staff for many years. In the move to educated self-help leading to a healthier workforce, it was decided to introduce in 1989 a programme called Risk Factor Screening.

Management staff have been offered health checks for many years. General staff over the age of 30 are now given the opportunity to talk and learn about themselves, and are therefore given the knowledge to make any changes to enhance their general health and performance.

We are nearing the end of the 5 year screening programme – where 32,500 people have been offered the test provided by AMI. A questionnaire is completed in discussion with an occupational health nurse. Blood pressure, weight and other measurements are taken, and a dry blood test for cholesterol is now used. At the end of ½ hour, each person will have a print out of their risk factors and a booklet discussing diet, exercise, smoking, alcohol and stress is given for further referral.

The benefit to our staff of the ½ hour of talking about themselves cannot be under-estimated, particularly in the current economic climate, where many are the bread winners for the family and are bringing the family problems to work with them. The uptake of this screening has now risen to over 90%.

The question we now have to ask is whether there has been any measurable change or benefit from this programme.

Store feedback tells us that following screening things have improved but we are about to embark on a 3-year re-screening programme to learn detailed lessons from what has been achieved.

Store-based Improvement Programmes

The improvement programme has been designed to encourage every employee in a store to make an active, on-going contribution to the improvement of the business. It is used in conjunction with, and supplements such other programmes as suggestion schemes and communication groups.

This particular programme provides a full methodology for involving employees at all levels, and across all stores in a structured and systematic group based on problem-solving activity. The employees' contributions are focused on very specific issues. They understand the issues and the benefits to be gained from meeting their targets. They are responsible for their own performance and will be committed to achieving success. It is empowerment by any other name.

Methodology

This is easy to implement and has the following structure.

Firstly, the goal is defined by the group. The constraints to achieving that goal are identified and improvements are made. The effects of these must be monitored and the results shared.

In order for you to fully understand the benefits of this approach, I will fit into this framework one of the pilot studies called 'The Marble Arch Project'.

Working on a food till can be seen by some as a mindless job but it is one of the most important from the Company's point of view. There is a specific need to raise the job satisfaction and self-esteem of the food sales assistants to help them achieve peak operational performance.

The project team decided that one of the factors causing problems was the length of time someone could spend on a till without a break. They decided their goal was to reduce the current average level from over 4 hours to 3 hours. This would mean that staff would be more willing to work on the tills, and would be fresher and more positive in their customer contact – reducing problems of fatigue and aches and pains.

The topic also raised a number of issues which also helped to improve the productivity of the food till area, and the morale of the staff.

They achieved their goal, absence levels fell and productivity and morale was improved.

This proved to be a simple but highly effective mechanism, the principles of which could be used in many contexts and circumstances.

Employee Assistance Programmes

To avoid being repetitive I will refer you back to when I mentioned 'in company' and external factors that pertained to Marks & Spencer personnel. We do indeed have 'specialists' of our own in both the personnel and occupational health teams who are able to counsel and deal with individual issues.

There are times, however, when those problems can move beyond that sphere of expertise and require something which can only be met by external resources.

The EAP programmes have come to us from America and seek to provide a solution to the problem of identifying a need – which may be hidden – and providing the correct solution for that particular issue.

Marks & Spencer has recently been looking at the question of EAP provision. At this stage we are not at liberty to detail our decisions, but there were some pertinent questions asked that may be of some use to others.

1. Should this be seen as a 'benefit' available to all staff, or used separately to cope with a problem?

2. Can the Company culture cope with an 'outsider' having detailed knowledge of problems and issues which hitherto had been the domain of the employer?

3. Should employees families be involved?

4. How can you monitor the quality of counselling and measure the success or value for money that both the individual and the organisation are getting?

5. Will employees benefit and use the system more *because* it is an outside confidential agency?

Managing Pressure

For many of the self-same reasons mentioned in the last section, it has become apparent that staff are facing a series of complex problems relating both to the workplace and the world around them.

There has been more change for staff in their working environment and personal lives in the last 2/3 years than before. It is far better that we teach them to cope, than having to use remedial programmes.

Our Occupational Health department when working with the consultant on the store based improvement initiative, identified the need to teach people to manage pressure. It is important that this is not seen in the context of stress management – I am deliberately calling this learning to manage pressure well before the unacceptable side of stress plays a part.

It is planned to include all levels of staff and the concept has passed from being embryonic to the first stages of development. I am hoping that the pilot studies will have been completed and evaluated over the next few months, and we will then be able to measure the rewards for the individual and the Company.

The Impact of Information Technology

We have seen the introduction of IT into the workplace over a relatively short period of time – but it has quickly become a natural and normal part of working life.

The Improvement Project described earlier was initiated in response to a concern that changes in computer based technology were affecting the workplace environment and creating additional pressures on the sales assistants. The drive for throughput and optimisation of staffing levels added to this pressure. The problem appeared to be most acute in the food area and manifested itself in a variety of ways including physical and mental health problems and a reduction in job satisfaction. These symptoms were brought to the attention of the occupational health department, who asked a consultant to study the impact of new technology on the food till operators.

The initial study was carried out in Autumn 1991, and resulted in the identification of a number of problems with the equipment which in turn were causing problems for the sales staff. These concerned:

* Till design and the working environment
* Till delays through incorrect handling
* Till delays as a result of Supervisor calls

The design problems could be solved by working with the equipment department and the supplier, and the working practices were addressed in a way that I previously outlined.

Clearly the impact can prove to be negative as well as positive. Anxiety at the new systems or the threat of ensuing redundancy, fear of coping with something unfamiliar particularly for older staff at the initial stages.

In these situations I would address you to three key areas.

1. Training – thorough and focused training is vital.

2. Equipment audit – making sure that the design meets the needs of the task and the individual. The European Direc-

tives have to some extent helped to bring this area into focus.

3. Working practices – that may have been in place for a long time may need to be examined and changed in the light of the new technology.

Secondments and Community Involvement

We run a programme that means approximately 25–30 people are on full time secondment during each year, as well as those who are part of the 100 hour programme run by Action Resource Centre for us. These will be a mixture of personnel at all levels, and at different stages of their career. For the purposes of this paper I will confine myself to mid career secondments, who are people too old for young development, and too young for pre-retirement.

In many cases these are staff who have been with the company for some length of time, and who may need to be revitalised, learn other skills, or simply benefit from another experience. Below are summarised the proven benefits both to the individual and to the company.

The individual learns to value themselves and their skills, as they see their performance in a different context. Quite often they are working in a small organisation having to take decisions which will determine the fate of that outfit, and as a result their decision making ability is enhanced. They come to have a different perspective on life – particularly when working with disadvantaged groups, and then there are new skills, and often an increased confidence. The company on the other hand then has its' ambassador who brings back new skills and fresh thinking, giving an added value to their performance.

The Wellness Forum

There are a number of organisations including Marks & Spencer who have joined together to form this forum. We intend to share developments, and to benefit from the experience of the other members – hopefully increasing the general wellbeing of our troops.

Looking to the Future

Several quite fundamental factors will have a lasting effect on the mental wellbeing of employees over the next five years. In shaping future policies we should have these issues in our minds.

1. Further changes in the working environment, and working practices will take place, and we should ensure that our staff are ready and able to respond.

2. The recruitment marketplace may well change, and with it the need to look more closely at policies which will be attraction and retention driven.

3. The importance of having corporate mental health policies – made up of a number of component parts. One of the most important will be the way that communication and decision-making takes place in the future, particularly now we are European.

4. The whole need to constantly audit the programmes that we develop, and the importance of quality assurance.

5. The move towards a conscious pro-active empowerment of the individual.

Defining the problem: Stress, Depression and Anxiety: Causes, Prevalence and Consequences

Rachel Jenkins

Introduction

This chapter aims to clarify some of the concepts we are using, and to cover the different kinds of psychological illness, what they look like, how common they are, how long they last, their prevalence in workplace settings, their causes and consequences, and implications for prevention.

Concepts of stress

So first of all, I would like to discuss what we mean by stress and by mental or psychological illness. I used to think 'stress' was a much abused term (and that it was only my definition which was correct!) until I discovered that the Oxford English Dictionary describes about 15 meanings of the word stress, several dating from the fourteenth century, so they all have a good provenance. For our purposes it helps to concentrate on three *(see Fig 1)*. The first is an external challenge (which can be a good thing). It means a stimulus, the notion of being stretched, or even of career development if you like. This is the meaning often used by Chief Executives who say, 'But surely stress is good for you – my staff aren't nearly stressed enough . . .'.

The second is external hardship and adversity (which when intolerable is a bad thing). This is the meaning often used by employees who say, 'I'm under a lot of stress just now. I wish the manager would stop piling it on' and is the meaning used by researchers interested in studying what factors in the workplace can cause such overload *(see Fig 2)*.

And the third meaning is the internal state induced within the individual by the external adversity, ie the distress or reaction of the person under stress. This is the meaning used by over-

Figure 1

Good pressure – able to cope

Figure 2

Bad pressure – unable to cope

Figure 3

And the effects!

whelmed employers who are experiencing physical and psychological symptoms, and who say 'I'm very stressed just now'. Thus the term 'stress' is being used to refer to either cause or effect, and this is the cause of much confusion in the literature, and in our own understanding of the concept *(see Fig 3)*. It explains why, when two or three people are gathered today, there will be two or three different meanings of the work 'stress' being used.

We therefore need to emphasise the distinction between stress which refers to environmental demands and pressures on us (what the OED calls external hardship and adversity) and stress which refers to the psychological and physical symptons which are the consequences of those environmental demands and pressures on us. The former sense is used in psychiatric academic literature on the causation of mental illness, the latter sense is greatly used in the occupational academic and lay literature. So, if you're going to have a discussion about stress, you need to define the term.

Mental disorder – its nature and extent

Now I want to look at the spectrum of stress and mental disorder. Stress in its sense of distress or symptoms is one end of a spectrum which moves from symptoms to illness to very severe illness *(see Fig 4)*. I would like to take each part of the spectrum in turn. What are these psychological symptoms, otherwise sometimes known as stress? They are listed in Fig 5 *(see Fig 5)*.

How common are these symptoms? The simple answer is that they are very common. *Table 1* gives data from a study of executive officers in the Civil Service. The symptoms which are extremely common are fatigue, irritability and poor concentration. These are all symptoms which we will be familiar with. Most of us have experienced some of them at some time or another. Poor concentration, not being able to concentrate for adequate periods, comes to notice more quickly in some jobs than in others, and may cause accidents. Fatigue may range from feeling tired on awakening, to feeling exhausted at the end of the day, to persistent fatigue. Irritability may range from snapping at colleagues and friends to rows or even violence.

A little less common are depression, anxiety, impaired sleep and appetite. Depressed mood can range from feeling low for an hour

Figure 4 The spectrum of stress and mental disorder

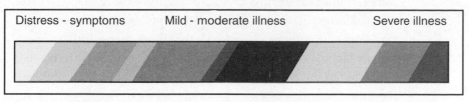

Distress - symptoms   Mild - moderate illness   Severe illness

Figure 5 Distress – symptoms

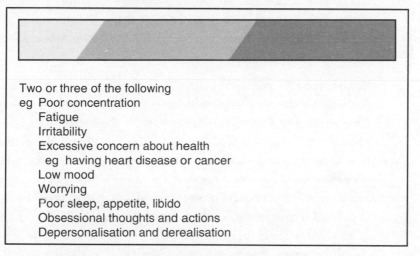

Two or three of the following
eg Poor concentration
      Fatigue
      Irritability
      Excessive concern about health
        eg having heart disease or cancer
      Low mood
      Worrying
      Poor sleep, appetite, libido
      Obsessional thoughts and actions
      Depersonalisation and derealisation

TABLE 1 *Prevalence of Psychological Symptoms in a Working Population of Executive Officers*

% With	Men	Women
Somatic symptoms	13.3 (24)	33.1 (46)
Excessive concern	10.2 (19)	16.4 (23)
Fatigue	23.9 (54)	36.7 (51)
Sleep disturbance	14.7 (27)	15.1 (21)
Irritability	21.6 (39)	26.4 (36)
Lack of concentration	37.0 (68)	26.9 (37)
Depression	28.0 (51)	38.9 (54)
Depressive thoughts	24.1 (44)	26.9 (37)
Anxieties	34.5 (63)	32.2 (44)
Phobias	12.8 (23)	15.5 (21)
Obsessions	18.5 (34)	16.2 (22)
Depersonalization	8.9 (16)	6.1 (8)

or two a day to a pervasive low mood which is difficult to snap out of, feeling like crying, crying (women cry more easily than do men). Things may look bleak and hopeless. Life may appear pointless and without pleasure so that there seems little value in living. Anxiety can range from minor worries to major persistent preoccupations. Sometimes people sleep too much, sometimes too little. Sleep can be patchy. There may be difficulty getting off to sleep at night or sometimes people may wake up too early in the morning. Somewhat less common still are obsessional thoughts and actions. These are repetitive thoughts or actions consciously resisted. Depersonalisation is the sensation that you yourself feel slightly unreal, derealisation is the sensation that the world around you feels unreal.

Returning to the middle section of our spectrum in Fig 4, what are the mild-moderately severe illnesses? They include depressive illness, anxiety states, mixed anxiety – depressive disorders, phobias and obsessional neuroses *(see Fig 6)*. What is the distinction between symptoms and illness, or, in other words, when does low mood become a depressive illness? This is of course an arbitrary manmade decision, as it is for high blood pressure, but in general terms, low mood becomes a depressive illness when it occurs with a cluster of other symptoms, when it lasts more than a couple of weeks and is difficult to snap out of, and when it is interfering with normal daily activities *(see Fig 7)*.

So a person with a mild-moderately severe depressive illness would have persistent low mood, tearfulness, inability to concentrate, fatigue, instability and disturbed sleep. He or she may be concerned that they have cancer or heart disease. Appetite and libido may be impaired. They may have one or two obsessional activities in the day, checking things several times, when once would do *(see Fig 8)*.

And a person with an anxiety state would not only be worrying about major crises, but also about a succession of minor trivia, besides the mental worry, they will describe physical manifestations such as sweaty palms, trembling, butterflies in the tummy, palpitations, pins and needles, and a frequent desire to urinate *(see Fig 9)*.

Returning now to the end section of our spectrum in Fig 4, what are the severe illnesses? They include depressive psychosis,

Figure 6 Mild – moderate illness

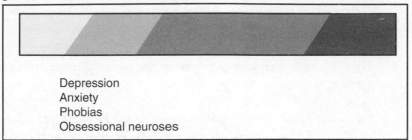

Depression
Anxiety
Phobias
Obsessional neuroses

Figure 7 When is low mood a depressive illness?

Persistent

Longer than two weeks

Accompanied by several other symptoms

Figure 8 What does a mild-moderate depressive illness look like?

Persistent low mood, difficult to snap out of

Feels like crying (men) or crying (women)

Unable to concentrate for long periods, so work piles up

Fatigue (tired every night, wakes up tired)

Irritable

Worrying about physical health

Impaired sleep

Figure 9 What does an anxiety state look like?

Persistent anxiety

Worry over trivia

Physical manifestations – sweaty palms
                       – trembling
                       – butterflies in tummy
                       – palpitations
                       – pins and needles
                       – frequent desire to urinate

manic depressive psychosis, schizophrenia and paranoid psychosis *(see Fig 10)*. The symptoms of these illnesses include extreme abnormality of mood, abnormal perceptions (hallucinations), abnormal beliefs (delusions) and thought disorder *(see Fig 11)*. These symptoms are rare in the working population *(see Table 2)*.

So, how common is mental illness overall? Most prevalence studies have been done on the general population in the community, and there are now many good epidemiological studies over the last 20 years, in both Western and Third World countries, showing that about 100–250 per 1,000 adults have a psychological disorder in any one year *(see Table 3)*. By far the majority of this is depression and anxiety, only 1–3% of this is psychosis of some kind, mostly schizophrenia and affective psychosis.

The number of epidemiological studies carried out in workplace settings is much lower, and is far lower in this country than in the US *(see Table 4)*. Those that exist tend to show roughly what you would expect, namely that those disorders which are common in the general population, ie depression and anxiety, are also common in people at work, while those disorders which are rare in the general population, are even rarer in working populations. So occupational doctors, like GPs, will tell you that the bread and butter of their work is depression and anxiety.

However, there is a paradox here which is not explained. We would expect prevalence rates to be higher in community studies (which include the unemployed) than in workplace studies. However the reverse is true. It is not a chance finding, because every workplace study done so far finds the same high rates. So is it that we have only studied stressful work environments so far, and that somewhere there exist more peaceful environments, or is there some other explanation?

Returning now to the end section of our spectrum in Fig 4, the severe mental illnesses include depressive psychosis, manic depressive psychosis, schizophrenia and paranoid psychosis. These illnesses are distinguished from the less severe by the extreme abnormalities of mood, by abnormal perceptions (hallucinations), abnormal beliefs (delusions) less than 1% of the general population, and are even less common in people at work.

Figure 10   Severe illness

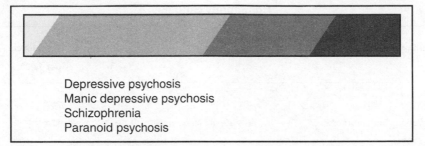

Depressive psychosis
Manic depressive psychosis
Schizophrenia
Paranoid psychosis

Figure 11   What are the symptoms of severe illness?

All the other symptoms may be present

and extreme abnormality of mood
    Abnormal perceptions (hallucinations)
    Abnormal beliefs (delusions)
    Thought disorder

What are the causes of mental illness?

The causes of psychological illness can be classified into psycho-logical, social and biological and it is helpful to think of them in terms of predisposing factors, ie factors which may have been operating literally years ago to make one more vulnerable to illness, precipitating factors, ie which precipitate the onset of illness, and maintaining factors, ie which prolong the illness (see Fig 12).

In order to understand this more readily, it can be useful to adopt a parallel with physical illness. Predisposing factors to chest infection may be a low immunity, smoking or allergy or exposure to chemicals. Precipitating factors may be a chill combined with exposure to a virus. Maintaining factors may be not resting, or a poor diet etc.

The very severe psychotic illnesses have a strong genetic contri-bution (up to about 50%), and we know that from studies of identical and non-identical twins who were adopted at birth. However, the non-psychotic illnesses, depression and anxiety don't have a genetic component. They are caused by environmen-tal stress of one kind and another, and by physical illness.

TABLE 3 *How Common is Mental Illness in the Community?*

Community Studies

Author	N	Place	Instrument	Prevalance per 1,000
Myers et al 1984	3,481	USA	DIS	267
Goldberg, Kay and Thompson (1974)	213	South Manchester	GHQ	184
Finlay, Jones and Burvill (1977)	2,342	Perth, Australia	GHQ	120
Ingham, Rawnsley and Hughes (1972)	300	Industrial Wales (Rhondda)	CMI	175
	581	Rural Wales (Vale of Glamorgan)		103
Dilling 1979	1,231	Bavaria, W Germany	CIS	193
Welssman, Myers and Harding 1978	511	Newhaven USA	SADS-RDC	178
Orley and Wing 1979	191	Ugandan Village	PSE	241
Duncan, Jones and Henderson 1980	756	Canberra, Australia	PSE	90
Brown and Harris 1978	458	Camberwell, London	PSE	170
Brown et al 1977	154	North Ulst, Outer Hebrides	PSE	120
Hodiamont et al 1987	486	Nijmegan, Holland	GHQ/PSE	73
Duncan-Jones and Henderson 1978	157	Canberra, Australia	GHQ/PSE	90
Bebbington et al 1981	800	London, England	PSE	109
Regier et al 1988	18,571	5 sites USA	DIS	112
Vazquez-Barquero et al 1987	425	Cantabria, Spain	PSE	147
Mavreas et al 1986	489	Athens, Greece	GHQ/PSE	160
Vazquez-Barquero et al 1981	415	Batzan Valley, Spain	CIS	239
Cheng 1988	489	3 areas: Taiwan	CHQ/CIS	262

Overall rates				164

Abbreviations: GHQ=General Health Questionnaire   SADS=Schedule for Affective Disorders and
CHQ=Chinese Health Questionnaire   Schizophrenia
PSE=Present State Examination   RDC=Research Diagnostic Criteria
DIS=Diagnostic Interview Schedule   CIS=Clinical Interview Schedule

TABLE 4 *How Common is Mental Illness in the Workplace?*

Author	N	Population	Instrument	Prevalence per 1,000		
				M	F	Total
Fraser R. 1947	3,000	Light and medium engineering workers	Medical assessment	283	360	300
Heron and Braithwaite 1953	184	Colliery workers	MMQ			
		Sedentary		334		
		Surface manual		452		
		Surface and underground		522		
Jenkins, MacDonald, Murray & Strathdee 1982	162	Times Journalists	CIS(GHQ)			
		I month after receipt of redundancy notice and 2 months prior to closure date.				378(360)
		At sale of newspaper when redundancy notices, revoked, and new proprietor arrived				378(369)
MacBride, Lancee and Freeman 1981	274	Air traffic controllers during an industrial dispute	GHQ			
		4 months later				
		10 months later				
Jenkins 1985a	184	Executive offIcers in Civil Service	CIS	362	343	
McGrath, Reid and Boore 1989	171	Nurses	GHQ			270
		Teachers				310
		Social workers				370
Stansfield, Marmot et al 1991	10,314	Whitehall civil servants (administrative grades	GHQ			
		1–7)		248	353	
		SEO, HEO, EO		247	331	
		Clerical		216	252	
Jenkins et al 1992	75	Whitehall civil servants (SEO, HEO and EO)	CIS			320

Figure 12 What are the causes of mental illness?

		Predisposing factors
Physical	–	genes, intrauterine, damage, birth trauma, personality disorder
Social	–	physical and emotional deprivation in childhood, due to bereavement, separation, family discord, chronic social difficulties at work and at home, lack of supportive relationships
Psychological	–	poor parental models, low self esteem

		Precipating factors
Physical	–	recent infections, disabling injury, malignant disease
Social	–	recent life events, eg threat of redundancy, unemployment, major illness in the family, a child leaving home, separation or divorce, and the loss of a supportive relationship
Psychological	–	maladaptive feelings of hopelessness, hopelessness

		Maintaining factors
Physical	–	chronic pain or disability, side effects of medication, failure to take medication
Social	–	chronic social stress, lack of social support
Psychological	–	low self esteem, lack of expectation of recovery

So you can see that the working environment is one of the environmental influences, operating for better or worse, on the predisposition, precipitation and maintenance of psychological illness. Later speakers will go on to describe in more detail the important stressors and supports in the occupational setting, but these can be broadly categorised into

1. factors intrinsic to the job
2. role in the organisation
3. career development
4. relationships at work
5. organisation structure and climate.

What kinds of social stress and support are there?

A useful way to categorise stress is by the different broad social domains of marriage or intimate relationship; the other members of the immediate relationship; the other members of the immediate family, including children; social life, that is friends and acquaintances, and leisure activities; housing and living conditions; finance and occupation *(see Fig 13)*. All these different domains can be stressful.

A second useful categorisation of stress is by duration of the event. Thus we sometimes refer to *acute life events* such as bereavement, or job loss, or failing an exam, while more long term *chronic stresses* would include loneliness, unemployment, poverty or illiteracy.

Each of these social domains can also be supportive. There are several different kinds of support that seem to matter, including emotional support, appraisal support, practical information, and instrumental help. So, it becomes clear that work is one of six social domains in which stresses and supports occur. In some people it is a very dominant domain where we spend more than eight hours a day, and to that extent is therefore a potent medium for better or worse.

Figure 13   What kinds of social stresses are there?

A classification of external stresses and support

SOCIAL FACTORS

Domains	Stress	Supports
Marriage		
Family		
Social Life/Friends		
Housing		
Finance		
Work		

I would like to emphasise that the cause of depression and anxiety is nearly always multifactorial and there will always be a number of causes operating.

Consequences of mental illness

For employers, this is generally an even more important consideration than the cause *(see Fig 14)*.

Firstly there are consequences for physical health. People with psychological disorders have an increased risk of physical illness, and indeed mortality, partly from physical disorders and partly from suicide. The risk of death from all causes is twice the norm in severe non-psychotic depression (Sims and Prior 1978) and the risk of death is four or five times the norm in schizophrenia and manic depressive psychosis, excluding suicide (Fox and Goldblatt 1982). The risk of suicide for minor depression and anxiety is not so very great, but for very severe mental illness it is substantial: 10% schizophrenia; 15% manic depression; 10% alcoholics.

Secondly there are domestic consequences.

Psychological illness may cause a variety of problems in the social domains of marriage, finance, housing, family life and social life. Thus those domains are not only the medium for stress and support, ie the causes of illness, they are also the medium for the consequences of illness. For example, continued depression or

Figure 14   Consequences of mental illness

1.   Increased risk of physical illness and death

2.   Domestic consequences
     marriage
     finance
     housing
     family life
     social life

3.   Occupational consequences
     sickness absence
     relations with colleagues
     work performance
     accidents
     labour turnover

irritability may place a great strain on the understanding and tolerance of a spouse, eventually leading to marital problems. If prolonged, this may cause more serious disruption of the relationship, and may occasionally lead to divorce, with far reaching long term consequences for children and for the joint finance.

The depressed person may become unable to manage his financial affairs, bills may remain unpaid and letters unanswered. Essential house repairs may not be carried out, leading to further deterioration in the property which could easily have been prevented. Parental illness can lead to conduct disorders and emotional disturbances in the children. Children are usually affected if both parents are simultaneously depressed for any length of time, but usually remain unscathed as long as one parent is well and fully functional. There is a tendency to withdraw from friendships when depressed, thus losing opportunities for social support. All these social consequences form a vicious circle which in turn acts as further stress on the individual, maintaining the illness. On a more optimistic note, occasionally an illness can provide an opportunity to rethink one's life, and reorder priorities, and that can be very positive.

Lastly but not least, there are the occupational consequences of psychological illness and these include sickness absence, impaired relations with colleagues, reduced work performance, accidents, labour turnover.

All of these have measurable social and economic costs, and because these costs may be used in the decision as to whether it is cost effective to initiate preventive strategies in the workplace, I would like to take a closer look at one common consequence, sickness absence. The sickness absence caused by mental health problems does not simply consist of that certified absence attributed on the certificate to mental illness. It also consists of certified absence attributed to physical health problems where the underlying mental health problem was either missed by the certifying doctor (GPs do not detect 50% of the psychological disorder that presents to them) or was detected, but not labelled as such on the certificate so as to avoid stigma and possible penalties by the employer. It also consists of uncertified absence due to psychological illness (see Jenkins 1992 for a fuller account).

A Model for Prevention

Fig 15 presents a simple model for the causation of mental illness. In the square box is the person, with their genes, their upbringing, their personality and their coping abilities. And acting on us, all the time, are the external stresses. We are also supported in a number of ways and, if things become unbalanced for too long, if the stresses outweigh the supports over a long period, then we start to develop symptoms which may lead on to illness, and then to the consequences of illness.

Fig 15 can now be used to examine where the possibility for prevention lies *(see Fig 16)*. Firstly, we can try to prevent workplace stresses. Secondly we can try to maximise the supports that are available to people (emotional support, appraisal support, giving information and instrumental support) in the workplace setting. Thirdly we can teach stress management techniques, to help people recognise when they are overloaded, and to deal with it appropriately. Fourthly, when illness has occurred, which it inevitably will from time to time, we can detect it very promptly

Figure 15   A model for the causation of mental illness

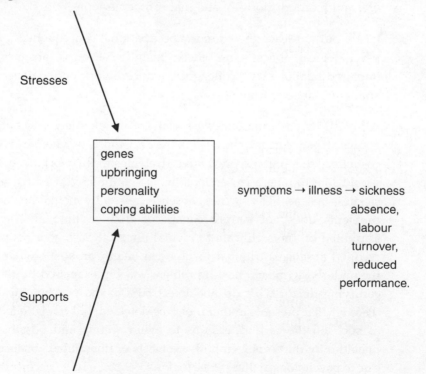

and manage it appropriately so that the person does not suffer for months or even years with untreated depression, with its attendant consequences for the workplace, but instead is quickly restored to full functioning again.

Figure 16   A model for the prevention of mental illness in the workplace

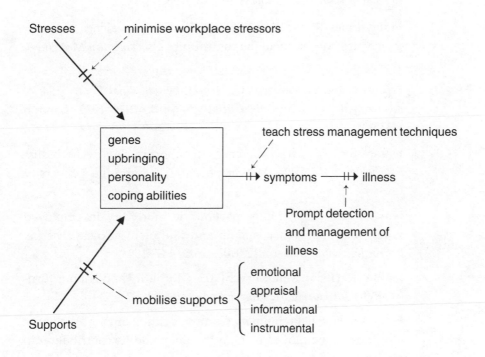

References

Bebbington P., Hurry J., Tennant C., Sturt E. and Wing J. (1981). Epidemiology of mental disorders in Camberwell. Psychological Medicine 11, 561–581.

Brown G. W. and Harris T. (1978). *social origins of depression*. A study of psychiatric disorder in women. London: Tavistock Press.

Cherniss C. (1980). *Staff burnout: Job Stress in the Human Services*. Beverley Hills, California. Sage Publications.

Cheng T. A. 91988). A community study of minor psychiatric morbidity in Taiwan. *Psychological Medicine* **18**, 953–968.

Cobb S. (1976). Social support as a Moderator of Life Stress. *Psychosomatic Medicine* **38**, 300–314.

Dilling H. (1980). Psychiatry and primary health services: results in a field survey. Acta Psychiatrica *Scandinavica Supplement* **No 285**, 62, 15–22.

Duncan Jones P. and Henderson P. (1978). The use of a two stage design in a prevalence survey. *Social Psychiatry*, **13**, 231–237.

Ferguson D. (1973). A study of neurosis and occupation. *British Journal of Industrial Medicine* **30**, 187–198.

Finlay-Jones R. and Burvill P. (1977). The prevalence of minor psychiatric morbidity in the community. *Psychological Medicine* **7**, 474–489.

Fox A. J. and Goldblatt P. O. (1982). *Longitudinal Study – Socio-demographic Mortality Differential LS No 1, 1971–1975*. London HMSO.

Jenkins R. (1985a). Sex differences in minor psychiatric morbidity. *Psychological Medicine Monograph No 7*, Cambridge University Press.

Jenkins R. (1985b). Minor psychiatric morbidity in employed young men and women, and its contribution to sickness absence. *british Journal of Industrial Medicine* **42**, 147–154.

Jenkins R. (1985). Minor Psychiatric Morbidity and Labour turn-over. *British Journal of Industrial Medicine* **42**, 534–539.

Jenkins R. (1980). Preliminary Communication: minor psychiatric morbidity in employed men and women and its contribution to sickness absence. *Psychological Medicine* **10**, 751–757.

Jenkins R., Macdonald A., Murray J. and Strathdee G. (1982). Minor psychiatric morbidity and the threat of redundancy in a professional group. *Psychological Medicine* **12**, 799–807.

Jenkins R., Mann A. H. and Belsey E. 91981). Design and use of a short interview to assess social stress and support in research and clinical settings. *social Science and Medicine 15E*, **3**, 195–203.

Johns G. and Nicholson N. (1982). *The meanings of absence: new strategies for theory and research In Research in Organisational Behaviour*. Eds B. M. Blair and L. L. Cummings, Greenwich: CTJAI Press.

MacBride A., Lancee W. and Freeman S. (1981). The Psychosocial Impact of a Labour Dispute, *Journal of Occupational Psychology* **54**, 125–133.

Mann A. H., Jenkins R. and Belsey E. (1981). The twelve month outcome of patients with neurotic illness in general practice. *Psychological Medicine* **11**, 535–550.

Mavreas V., Beis A., Mouijias A., Rigeni F. and Lyketsas G. (1986). Prevalence of psychiatric disorders in Athens: A community study. *Social Psychiatry* **21**, 172–181.

McDermott D. (1984). Professional Burnout and its relation to job characteristics, Satisfaction and Control. *Journal of Human Stress* 79–85.

McGrath A., Reid N. and Boore J. (1989). Occupational Stress in Nursing. *International Journal of Nursing Studies* **26**, 343–358.

Myers J. K., Weissman M. M., Tischler G. L. et al (1984). Six month prevalence of psychiatric disorders in three communities. *Archives of General Psychiatry* **41**, 959–67.

Orley J. and Wing J. (1979). Psychiatric disorder in two African villages. *Archives of General Psychiatry* **36**, 513–520.

Regier D., Boyd J., Burke J., Rae D., Myders J., Kramer M., Robins L., George L., Karno M. and Locke B. (1988). One month prevalence of mental disorders in the United States. *Archives of General Psychiatry* **45**, 977–985.

Sims A. and Prior P. (1978). The pattern of mortality in severe neuroses. *british Journal of Psychiatry* **133**, 299–305.

Stansfield S. and Marmot M. (1991) (unpublished). Whitehall II study of civil servnts.

Vazquez-Barquero J., Munoz P. and Madoz Jauregi V. (1981). The interaction between physical illness and neurotic morbidity in the community. *british Journal of Psychiatry* **139**, 328–335.

Vazquez-Barquero J., Diez-Mannique J. F., Pena C., Aldama J., Samaniego Roderiginez C., Menandez Arango J. and Mirapeix C. (1987). A community mental health survey in Canbalima a general description of morbidity. *Psychological Medicine* **17**, 227–241.

Weissman M., Myers J. and Harding P. (1978). psychiatric disorders in a US urban community: 1975/76. *American Journal of Psychiatry* **135**, 459–462.

6

DEFINING THE PROBLEM: WHAT EMPLOYEES WANT

Michael Craft

Introduction

Without going through a careful process of asking them, it is not possible to say 'what employees want' in relation to mental health at work. It is however important to focus on the critical importance of making the necessary enquiries. In describing this process two assumptions can be made: first that mental health *at* work is synonomous with mental health *and* work, or put another way, the world of work has the potential to be both good and bad for health. Thus when asking employees what they want, it is important to recognise this difference and its potential impact on employee perceptions. An employee that already has a mental health problem may gain immeasurably from being at work and in contact with a supportive team. Secondly, mental health is about achieving autonomy and control over ones own life. In this respect it will therefore be important for example, to include in any investigations, how control over work and teamworking feature in the workplace.

Mental health, employment and mental illness

There exists an undeniable link between the working environment and mental illness as well as mental health: correlations have been found in both directions. In 1990 80 million working days were lost due to sickness certified as mental illness: £1.7 billion was spent on mental illness services and 23% of pharmaceutical costs were for mental illness[1]. There is a growing body of evidence linking unemployment with health generally[2]. For example the unemployed have higher death rates – 1500 extra deaths for each million men unemployed; a two fold increase in suicides; a deterioration in mental health with becoming unemployed and a subsequent improvement with re-employment.

The importance of work emerges clearly from the 'People First' Survey carried out by MIND amongst 500 users of mental health services in 1990[3]. 80% of this sample first experienced problems before the age of 35 and at that time 53% were employed. But at the time of the survey only 16% were employed and the large difference of 37% represents people who lose their jobs or may become unemployed due to the effects of medication or stigma. If so many people lose employment as illness progresses, a considerable challenge exists.

Table 1

When was problem first experienced?	aged < 35	80
	employed then	53
Employed now		16
Social consequences	↓ self confidence	82
	↓ relationships in family	73.6
	↓ with friends	59.3
	↓ finances	58.3
	↓ education	34.9
Problems first discussed with	GP	35
	family	22
	psychiatrist	20
First contact with services via	GP	60
	police	8
	psychiatrst	6
	social worker	4
	friend	2

n = 500   MIND/ Roehampton Institute People First Survey, 1990

Table 1 shows that this survey reveals the huge impact of mental illness on relationships and self confidence, matters intimately linked to autonomy and likely to be critical in the working situation. Perhaps even more interesting is the finding that work colleagues, managers or occupational health are not mentioned as persons with whom problems were first discussed or services sought – here again is the challenge for prevention and support. If stress overload at work is a consideration, the literature shows several important effects: poor working relationships, low morale, low productivity, higher accidents, lateness, absenteeism, illness, disputes, vandalism, sabotage, higher labour turnover, higher requests for early retirement[4]. Other studies show that mental ill health at work is associated with **job design** (role strain, lack of autonomy or control over work, social support, work overload) and **organisational culture** (autocratic styles, lack of team working, poor communications, individual vulnerability)[5, 6, 7, 8, 9]. All of these features are therefore important reasons for first asking employees what they want before making plans.

Stress at work is undoubtedly an important problem. For example a recent Lifestyle Survey in Merton and Sutton District Health Authority amongst a representative sample of 2200 adults showed that 42% of the sample mentioned stress at work and only 22% said they coped with stress 'very well'[10]. In another survey in the North West Region amongst 3500 NHS employees randomly chosen, only 58% said they normally slept well and 11% used alcohol, 6% used sleeping pills to help them get to sleep, at least monthly[11]. But striking evidence of the connection between stress and work or lack of it has been provided by a large Lifestyle survey currently running in the Trent Region[12]. This survey, the largest of its kind ever carried out by a health authority, was based on a representative sample of 21,000 adults drawn from FHSA patients lists. Table 2 shows the results obtained when asking respondents what they felt stressed by, and the categories of 'work or unemployment', 'money' and 'fear of unemployment' are very high on the list.

Table 2

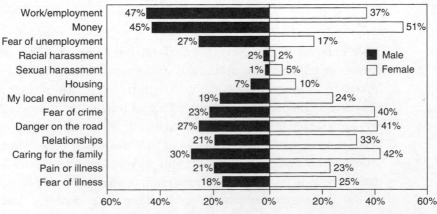

n = 11,732. males = 5,054 females = 6,678   Trent Health Lifestyle Survey 1992

This survey shows that young people are particularly stressed by 'work or unemployment' and 'money', and middle aged men by 'fear' of unemployment, as might be expected. In Table 3 a social class analysis of this data separates the unemployed from others and shows the greater impact felt by those out of work.

Table 3

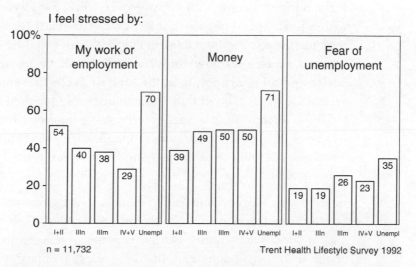

I feel stressed by:

n = 11,732   Trent Health Lifestyle Survey 1992

This survey also looked at the importance of social relationships in health and has relevance for the sorts of enquiries to be made in any needs assessment of employees. For example, as Table 4

Table 4

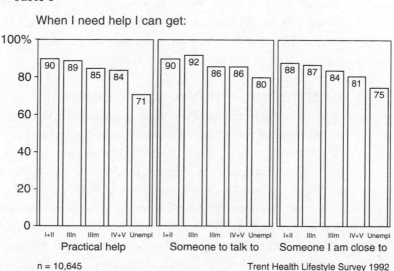

When I need help I can get:

n = 10,645   Trent Health Lifestyle Survey 1992 shows those not in work are less likely to be able to get simple information ('practical help'), to be able to talk something through ('someone to talk to'), or have access to intimacy ('someone I am close to').

The unemployed were also the least likely to have all three.

This data supports the work of Marmot et al[7] who found that social support (along with control over work) was associated with coronary heart disease in lower grades amongst 10,000 civil servants. Clearly the Trent data shows that **work provides social support, underlines how important work can be for mental health and therefore points to the kind of needs that could be assessed**. Boy[13] showed that work contributes to mental health for those already ill in a variety of ways: enhances treatment, improves self concept, provides socialisation and approval, develops discipline and helps gain insight for training and development.

In summary, employment can provide a positive as well as a negative impact on mental health and key aspects of job design and organisational culture can be targeted. Asking employees about their perceptions can therefore play a critical part in deciding what to target and it can also be an important instrument for staff participation. Surprisingly however the views of employees are not often sought, or if they are, the literature contains very few references to publication of such investigations that may be commissioned by employers. An exception is the survey carried out by Webb & Schilling[14] with employers and Trade Unions which showed action on stress (as well as alcohol and smoking which are frequently associated with it) to be high on their list of priorities for health at work.

Staff participation and Needs Assessment

It is obvious from the above that assessing the perceptions and needs of staff is not only desirable, but essential in planning for improved mental health at work. Sir Donald Maitland, as chair of the Health Education Authority, made clear at a recent seminar entitled 'Action on Health at Work',[15] that it is essential to establish the needs and wishes of employees before embarking upon any workplace health promotion activity. Needs assessment is frequently discussed as a tool for staff participation in health matters[4, 16] but less frequently carried out. A useful publication from the HEA[4] quotes a prominent employer recommending it:

'Top management must know how good or bad employees working conditions are. They must eat in the employees restaurants, visit the washrooms. If they are not good enough for those in charge they are not good enough for anyone.'

Lord Sieff, Marks & Spencer 1990

and an unknown ex employee regretting its absence;

'I suppose I was made redundant because I make poor quality cars. But in sixteen years, not once was I even asked for a suggestion as to how to do my job better. Not once.'

Car assembly line worker

Many companies are now promoting schemes that seek staff views and participation. Many studies suggest that needs assessment has value in **sharing concern about health between management and staff, increasing staff ownership of initiatives, allowing realistic and cost effective solutions to be adopted, assisting in the acceptance of priorities, agendas and timetables, as well as revealing those styles of management and culture that may be the most favourable to mental health at work**. Indeed in its 'Health at Work in the NHS' initiative (as part of the 'Health of the Nation' strategy) the present UK government spells out the need for staff needs assessment in its objectives:

'Investigate staff perceptions of organisational issues such as work patterns, employment policies, physical environment, communications systems, job design, workloads and role conflicts.'

and

'Prioritise these issues in consultation with staff in any subsequent health promotion intiatives.'

Objectives for Government Health at Work in the NHS Initiative, 1992

Dooner[17] suggest that such assessment must include questions about lifestyle (health and work attitudes, health practices); about surroundings (physical environment); issues and questions about self efficiency (sense of control over work) and says:

'conducting a needs assessment eliminates conjecture and provides for efficient planning . . . provides a focus for programme developers. It enables priorities to be ordered in relation to availability of resources'

It follows from this and the work quoted from the Trent Lifestyle Survey that questions about staff circumstances and experience **outside work** are of central importance. These contexts will help to assess the likely variation of needs manifest whilst at work and the psychosocial burden brought into work. This will in turn help to decide upon appropriate initiatives, for example in management training, occupational health schemes, confidential counselling, team building and job design. Without data on broad socio economic matters it is difficult to see how needs assessment can be a realistic guide to action. The actual process of needs assessment can be simple or more complex and the first may be a precursor for the latter:

Staff Needs Assessment

- Simple consultation   – suggestions box
  - surveys, interviews
  - regular management reports
  - newsletters, magazines

- Structural participation – job appraisal and redesign
  - teamworking
  - autonomous worker groups
  - quality circles
  - joint planning and involvement in health at work schemes

Jee & Reason, 1988

The UK Employment Act 1982 requires annual reports from companies employing more than 250 people or more, to describe arrangements for involving employees and the Institute of Personnel Management issues guidelines for such activity. Autonomous work groups that promote control over work have been in existence for some time in Sweden, Germany and in a few UK companies whilst quality circles are being practised in some 200 UK companies. It is reported that these kind of staff involvement lead to increased staff satisfaction, decreased absenteeism and disputes, and increased mental health[5].

Conducting a realistic staff assessment is likely in some instances to encounter resistance, and this must be taken into account. For example some autocratic companies or managers may perceive the exercise as threatening their own sense of control and may create some anxiety amongst employees who fear 'speaking out of turn'. Many managers lack training (fewer than 10% of the 2.7 million UK managers have ever been trained) and this may result in resistance to seeking staff views. The exercise needs some time and resources and there may be a temptation to seek views but not feedback or publish the results for fear of raising expectations. On reflection, any organisation contemplating a staff needs assessment will be able to see that the exercise itself can be used to allay such fears since the literature shows the enormous benefits of staff participation and ownership of any health initiatives. Managers who resist do so at risk of deteriorating staff relationships and their own credibility.

The South West Thames Regional Health Authority Staff Needs Assessment Census[16]

The region covers an area of SW England, including SW London and contains some 3 million people. Whilst a series of ad hoc activities and commitments to workplace health have existed for some time (the Look After Your Heart Charter, No Smoking Policy, Child Care Scheme, Occupational Health Sessions) no systematic plan or policy was being used. In 1991 a full census of the regional workforce (at HQ and outposts of the RHA) was planned as a way of establishing staff health perceptions and needs. The aim was to provide information for occupational health initiatives and for a programme of comprehensive health at work activities from the most simple to more complex and structural changes in communication training and teamworking.

A cross directorate working party planned and organised the work, first conducting its own interviews with senior managers to ensure their understanding and ownership of the exercise and then selected an agency (the London Research Centre) to carry out the detailed work. A full literature review was undertaken which showed that health is affected by work and correlated with grade, social support, lifestyle and socio economic status. The case for action was convincing and health at work programmes justify costs. Activity in the UK was patchy but 'Health of the Nation' represented a new opportunity.

A series of pilot interviews were held followed by a full scale postal questionnaire, not to a sample, but to **all** employees except those working for two groups under separate management arrangements or whose actual workplace was at district rather than regional level. The total numbers involved was 657 and a 75% response to the main instrument was obtained. This was found to be representative of the whole group in terms of gender, age and grade. 59% of the respondents were women and 41% men; a third were 29 or younger. More than 50% had worked for SWT two years or less.

70% felt their mental and physical health was affected 'a lot' or 'a certain amount' by work (mostly for the worse) with managers being most likely to believe this and junior grades least likely.

85% said that the workplace was highly appropriate as a place to improve health;

'a healthy workplace make people work better'

'we spend a lot of time here'

'health care is about valuing people'.

An important finding was that a significant minority of older employees in lower grades did **not** think workplace health policies would help much, perhaps indicating a lower level of expectation amongst this group. Significantly for mental health nearly two thirds of senior managers complained of high level of pressure and stress – more than twice as much as in more junior grades. Negative pressures arose from tedious, repetitive work, competing demands, the pace of change and uncertainty in the NHS, lack of communication and consultation both within the RHA and outside. Whilst two thirds of staff thought they had a good deal to say in **how** and **when** they did their work, there was a considerable dissatisfaction with **who decides** their work – the issue of control over work. So whilst this survey found high levels of commitment to the NHS (important for job satisfaction) stress was found to be high especially at senior levels with many implications for mental health.

Much of the problem was related to the physical environment: work space, how it was shared, insufficient privacy, open plan offices, heating, air quality, ventilation, the effects of VDU screens, clutter, wiring, cabling. Apart from a variety of needs expressed for more health checks and advice, healthy food, exercise and leisure facilities, respondents overwhelmingly believed it was important for **both** staff and management to be in favour and actively involved. A **minority** (44%) believed more money was needed. Most felt that making time available for health was important and this result supports the idea that organisational culture is a key determinant for mental health.

Following the completion of the census, a process of consultation was undertaken with staff in all locations to seek feedback on the results and draft recommendations. This process of staff involvement sought to refine and focus suggested changes, establish trust and ownership.

The following final recommendation were passed to the senior executives for action:

The Process:

* Ensure a systematic framework for staff involvement and feedback;
* negotiate conflicts of interest and take account of raised expectations;
* co-ordinate an integrated inter-directorate approach to health initiatives;
* clarify the role of occupational health service alongside everyday managerial responsiblities;
* recognise the impact of external lifestyles and socio-economic influences;

The Content:

* Use a policy framework to avoide victim blaming;
* address the psycho social issues: stress management, relaxation, management style, communications;
* address the work environment issues: office layout, clutter, noise, ventilation, lighting, heating control, equipment, furniture.
* Celebrate the positive aspects of the SWT psycho social environment and achievement to date.

Most of these ideas, build on the central notion that mental health at work is related to practical help in the form of occupational medicine, confidential support, increased teamworking and a supportive organisational culture.

Conditions in the NHS at the time of this work were producing very high levels of stress as was found by Cooper and Sutherland in 1990 [18] and by Rees and Cooper in 1990 [19]. It remains to be seen if action at the workplace level in a regional health authority can bring about improvement, without significant changes in the overall culture of the NHS which currently expects high level of 'delivery' from senior managers. As can be seen from this staff needs assessment, these same managers are showing higher levels of mental distress than other employees, and whilst they may have access to more social support and general help, it is they who are simultaneously expected to lead on the issue at work with colleagues and team members. Quite a tall order for people who are in the business of organising health care for the population. The recommendations were therefore set in a holistic context in order to maximise their effect in an uncertain climate: facilitation rather than direction; seeking support for local solutions rather than central direction; giving guidance and examples of good practice rather than policing; encouraging policies for individual healthy choices rather rules and coercive infrastructures.

References

1. *General Household Survey* (1990) OPCS.

2. Warr, P. B. (1987) *Work, Unemployment and Mental Health*. OUP.

3. Rogers, A. Pilgrim, D. & Lacey, R. (1993) Experiencing Psychiatry: users views. Mind/Macmillan, London.

4. Jee, M. & Reason, E. (1992) *Action on Stress at Work*. Health Education Authority, London.

5. Isaksson, K. (1989). Unemployment, mental health and the psychological function of work. *Scand. J.Soc. Medicine*. 17:2

6. Cooper, & Roden, J. (1985). Medicine health and satisfaction amongst tax officers. *J.Social Medicine*. 21:7

7. Marmot, M. G., et al (1991). Health Inequalities among British Civil Servants: the Whitehall II Study. *The Lancet* 337 8.6.91.

8. Cooper, C. & Cox, A. (1985). *Occupational stress amongst word processor operators*. Stress & Medicine. 1:2

9. McLean, A. (1982). *Improving mental health at work*. Psychiatric Hospital. 13:3

10. Martin, J. & Rawaf, S. (1992). *Lifestyle Survey*. Department of Public Health. Merton & Sutton District Health Authority.

11. North West Regional Health Authority. (1992). *Health at Work*: survey of NHS staff.

12. Trent Regional Health Authority. (1992). *Lifestyle Survey*.

13. Boy, A. V. (1987). Work and unemployment amongst mental health clients. *J. of Employment counselling*. 24:2

14. Webb, T. & Schilling, R. (1988). *Health at Work?* Research Report No. 22. HEA, London.

15. Health Education Authority. (1992). *Action on Health at Work*. HEA, London.

16. South West Thames Regional Health Authority. (1993). *Health at Work:* a staff Needs Assessment Census.

17. Dooner, B. (1990). *Achieving a healthier workplace – organisational action for individual health*. Health Promotion. Winter 2:6

18. Sutherland, V. J. & Cooper, C. (1992). Job stress, satisfaction and mental health amongst general practitioners before and after introduction of a new contract. *Brit. Med. J.* 304: 6841.

19. Rees, D. W. & Cooper, C. (1990). *Occupational stess in health service employee*. Health Service Management Research 3:3.

7

Finding The Solution—Primary Prevention (Identifying the causes and preventing mental ill health in the workplace)

Cary Cooper

Introduction

A WHO report (Kalimo, et. al. 1982) has suggested that alcoholism, coronary artery disease, mental ill health and a wide range of other stress-related illnesses in the workplace are costing industry throughout the world billions of dollars. A few years ago, the Centre for Health Economics estimated that over £1.3 billion alone in the UK is lost each year due to alcoholism in industry (£641.51m as a result of sickness absence, £567.70m due to premature death, etc.). In addition, WHO have published figures which indicate that not only is the United Kingdom near the top of the world league table in terms of mortality due to heart disease, for both men and women, but also is showing substantial yearly increases (Sutherland and Cooper, 1991). On the other hand, countries like the United States and Finland are showing substantial declines for the first time this century, which coincides directly with the introduction in industry of health promotion and stress management programmes for all employees. But why is the UK so far behind? Why is it that many countries, for example the US, seem to be showing declines in their levels of stress-related illnesses (eg heart disease, alcoholism), while the UK is still rising or at an unacceptably high level? Is it the case that American employers, for example, are becoming more altruistic and caring for their employees, and less concerned about 'the bottom line'? Not really, two trends in the US are forcing American firms to take action. First, American industry is facing an enormous and ever-spiralling bill for employee health care costs. Individual insurance costs rose by 50 per cent over the past two decades, but the employers' contribution rose by over 140 per cent. It has also been estimated that over $700 million a year is spent by American employers to replace the 200,000 men aged 45 to 65 who die or are incapacitated by coronary artery disease alone. In the UK, however, employers can create intolerable levels of stress on their employees, and it's the taxpayer who picks up the bill, through the National Health Service. There is no direct accountability or incentive for firms to maintain the health of their employees. Of course, the indirect costs are enormous, but rarely does the firm actually attempt to estimate this cost; they treat absenteeism, labour turnover and even low productivity as an intrinsic part of running a business (Dale and Cooper, 1992).

Second, there is another source of growing costs, too. More and more employees, in American companies at least, are litigating against their employers, through the worker compensation regulations and laws, in respect of job-related stress, or what is being termed 'cumulative trauma'. For example, in California, the stress-related compensation claims for psychiatric injury now total over 3,000 a year, since the California Supreme Court upheld its first stress-disability case in the early 1970s. The California labour code now states specifically that workers' compensation is allowable for disability or illness caused by 'repetitive mentally or physically traumatic activities extending over a period of time, the combined effect of which causes any disability or need for medical treatment'. California may be first; but what happens there has a habit of reaching other places after a longer or shorter time-lapse (Ivancevich, et. al, 1985).

In the UK, we are just beginning to see a move toward greater litigation by workers about their conditions of work. Several unions are supporting cases by individual employees, and the trend is certainly in the direction of future disability claims and general damages being awarded on the basis of 'stress at work' in the UK.

Stress Interventions in the Workplace

So what can we do to manage and prevent workplace stress. De Frank and Cooper (1987) suggest that interventions can focus on the individual, the organisation or the individual/organisational interface. Murphy (1988) emphasizes three levels of intervention: primary (eg, stressor reduction), secondary (eg stress management) and tertiary (eg, Employee Assistance Programs).

Figure 1   Levels of Stress Interventions and Outcomes

Interventions	Outcomes
Focus on individual:	Focus on individual:
Relaxation techniques	Mood states (depression, anxiety)
Cognitive coping strategies	Psychosomatic complaints
Biofeedback	Subjectively-experienced stress
Meditation	Physiological parameters (blood
Exercise	pressure, catecholamines, muscle
Employee Assistance Programmes	tension)
(EAPs)	Sleep disturbances
Time management	Life satisfaction
Focus on individual/organisational interface:	Focus on individual/organisational interface:
Relationships at work	Job stress
Person environment fit	Job satisfaction
Role issues	Burnout
Participation and autonomy	Productivity and performance
	Absenteeism
Focus on organisation:	Turnover
Organisational structure	Health care utilisation and claims
Selection and placement	
Training	Focus on organisation:
Physical and environmental charac-	Productivity
teristics of job	Turnover
Health concerns and resources	Absenteeism
Job rotation	Health care claims
	Recruitment/retention success

Source: DeFrank and Cooper 1987

Because historically the indices and costs of occupational stress (eg, medical insurance premiums) are more easily accessible and quantifiable than in other economies, the US has increasingly led the way in introducing initiatives to reduce stress and improve employee health in the workplace. According to Elkin and Rosch (1990): 'Increasingly, the workplace is seen as an appropriate and logical setting for developing and sustaining positive health practices'.

Most workplace initiatives operate at the secondary or tertiary levels. At the tertiary level, interventions fall into two main categories: health promotion activities and health screening. Health promotion/education programmes aim to modify behaviourial risk factors that lead to disease and poor health. Whereas health screening is concerned with the diagnosis and detection of existing conditions. In a recent survey of some 3000 worksites the US Department of Health and Human Services found that more than 60% of worksites with 750 or more employees now offer some form of stress management or health promotion activity. The form these activities take varies widely. It may involve the provision of keep fit facilities on site, dietary control, cardiovascular fitness programmes, relaxation and exercise classes, stress education or psychological counselling or some combination of these packages as a multi modular Employee Assistance Program (EAP).

Such initiatives by their definition, EAP, have tended to be 'employee' rather than 'organisation' directed strategies, whereby the focus is directed at changing the behaviours of the individual and improving their lifestyles and/or stress management skills. The interactionist approach (Cox, 1978; Cooper, Cooper and Eaker, 1988) depicts stress as the consequences of the 'lack of fit' between the individual and his/her environment. However, the emphasis of most workplace intervention strategies is to improve the 'adaptability' of the individual to the environment. Often described as 'the band-aid' or inoculation approach, there is an implicit assumption that the organisation will not change but continue to be stressful, therefore, the individual has to develop and strengthen their resistance to that stress. There appears to be markedly less organisational concern with adapting the environment to 'fit' the individual. One reason for this may be that the professional 'interventionists', the counsellors, physicians and clinicians are more comfortable with changing individuals than changing organisations (Ivancevich et. al, 1990).

What this chapter is attempting to do is posit the view that a more primary-orientated approach is needed in UK industry, one that attempts to identify the *sources* of workplace stress in order to intervene to change them. In other words, in order to move from cure to prevention, it is necessary to carry out diagnostic work or 'stress audits', not only so one can appropriately intervene to change the organisational stressors, but also to identify the early signs of stress to take preventative action.

The purpose of this chapter is to highlight what research has found to be some of the major sources of workplace stress. In addition, we will explore one example of a US intervention that has been successful.

Stressors in the workplace

Recent research (Cooper & Payne, 1988; 1991) has shown that there are many factors implicated in workplace stress. What follows is a brief summary of each of these.

Factors Intrinsic to the Job

Sources of stress intrinsic to the job across a variety of occupations include poor physical working conditions, shift work, work overload or underload, physical danger, and person-job mismatch.

Poor physical working conditions can enhance stress at work. In a study carried out on the factors associated with casting in a steel manufacturing plant, it was found that poor physical working conditions were a major stressor. Many of the pressures were concentrated in the physical aspects of noise, fumes, and to a lesser extent, heat, plus the social and psychological consequences of isolation and interpersonal tension (Kelly and Cooper, 1981). In the Three Mile Island Accident, researchers found that excessive emergency alarms and poor ergonomics were implicated in the human error leading to the accident (Cooper and Smith, 1985).

Numerous occupational studies have found that shift work is a common occupational stressor, as well as affecting neuro-physiological rhythms, such as blood temperature, metabolic rate, blood sugar levels, mental efficiency, and work motivation, which may ultimately result in stress-related disease. A study by American researchers on air traffic controllers found four times the prevalence of hypertension, and also more mild diabetes and peptic ulcers, among controllers than in a comparable control group. Although these authors identified a range of job stressors as being instrumental in the causation of these stress-related maladies, shift work was isolated as a major problem area (Crump, et. al, 1980).

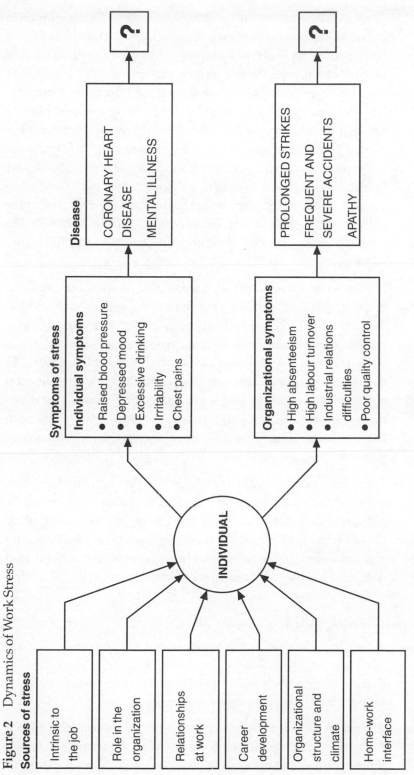

Figure 2 Dynamics of Work Stress

Source: Cooper, Cooper & Eaker (1988) *Living with Stress*. London: Penguin Books.

Work overload can be either quantitative (ie having too much to do) or qualitative (ie being too difficult), and certain behavioural malfunctions have been associated with job overload. In a study carried out among British police officers, it was found that workload was a major stressor among the lower ranks, particularly police sergeants. In particular, sergeants who scored high on the depression scale of the Middlesex Hospital Questionnaire tended to be older operational officers who believed they were overloaded, and who perceived a number of bureaucratic and outside obstacles to effective police functioning. They complained about the long hours and heavy work load, as well as the increased paperwork, lack of resources and the failure of the courts to prosecute offenders (Cooper, Davidson and Robinson, 1980).

Job underload associated with repetitive, routine, boring, and understimulating work has been associated with ill health. Moreover, in certain jobs, such as airline pilots, air traffic control, etc., periods of boredom have to be accepted, along with the possibility that one's duties may suddenly be disrupted due to an emergency situation. This can give a sudden jolt to the physical and mental state of the employee and have a subsequent detrimental effect on health. Furthermore, boredom and disinterest in the job may reduce the employee's response to emergency situations.

There are certain occupations which have been isolated as being high risk in terms of potential danger, eg police, mine workers, airline pilots, soldiers, and fireman. However, stress induced by the uncertainty of physically dangerous events is often substantially relieved if the employee feels adequately trained and equipped to cope with emergency situations.

Role in the Organisation

A person's role at work has been isolated as another main source of occupational stress, involving role ambiguity (ie conflicting job demands), responsibility for people and conflicts stemming from lack of clarity of organisational boundaries.

The problems that role conflicts can generate were amply demonstrated in a study of US dentists. It was found that the variables which predicted abnormally high blood pressure among dentists were factors related to the role of the dentist: (1) They feel their patients perceive them 'an inflictor of pain' rather than 'healer'; (2) They have to be managers, performing a range of non-clinical tasks such as administrative duties, sustaining and building a practice; and (3) their role also interferes with their personal life, primarily in terms of time commitments (Cooper, Mallinger and Kahn, 1978).

Career Development

The next group of organisationl stressors is related to career development, which has been found to be a fundamental stressor at work, and refers to 'the impact of overpromotion, under promotion, lack of job security, and thwarted ambition'. For example, career development blockages, have been found to be a significant stressor among women managers. In a large UK study, the researchers collected data from over 700 female managers and 250 managers at all levels of the organisational hierarchy and from among several hundred companies. It was found that women suffered significantly more than men on a range of organisational stressors, but the most damaging to their health and job satisfaction were the ones associated with career development and allied factors (eg sex discrimination in promotion, inadequate training, male colleagues treated more favourably, not enough delegation to women) (Davidson and Cooper, 1992).

Relationships at Work

Relationships at work, which include the nature of relationships and social support from one's colleagues, boss and subordinates, have also been related to job stress. According to University of Michigan researchers, poor relationships with other members of an organisation may be precipitated by role ambiguity in the organisation, which in turn may produce psychological strain in the form of low job satisfaction. Moreover, they found that strong social support from peers, relieved job strain and also served to condition the effects of job stress on cortisone levels, blood pressure, glucose levels and the number of cigarettes smoked (as well as cessation of cigarette smoking) (French, Caplan and Harrison, 1982).

In addition, where male executives had problems they were associated with problems in relationships, as the author and a

69

colleague discovered in their study of 196 very senior UK male executives (Cooper and Melhuish, 1980). It was found that male executives' predispositions (eg outgoing, tough-minded, etc.) and their relationships at work were central to their increased risk of high blood pressure. They were particularly vulnerable to the stresses of poor relationships with subordinates and colleagues, lack of personal support at home and work, and to the conflicts between their own values and those of the organisation.

Organisational Structure and Climate

Another potential source of occupational stress is related to organisational structure and climate, which includes such factors as office politics, lack of effective consultation, lack of participation in the decision-making process and restrictions on behaviour. US and UK researchers have found that greater participation led to higher productivity, improved performance, lower staff turnover and lower levels of physical and mental illness (including such stress related behaviours as 'escapist drinking' and 'heavy smoking').

Home: Work Pressures

Another danger of the current economic situation is the effect that work pressures (such as fear of job loss, blocked ambition, work overload and so on) have on the families of employees. At the very best of times, young managers, for example, face the inevitable conflict between organisational and family demands during the early build-up of their careers. But during a crisis of the sort we are currently experiencing, the problems increase in geometrical proportions as individuals strive to cope with some of their basic economic and security needs. Individuals under normal circumstances find 'home' a refuge from the competitive and demanding environment of work, a place where they can get support and comfort. However, when there is a career crisis (or stress from job insecurity as many employees are now facing), the tensions the individuals bring with them into the family affect the spouse and home environment in a way that may not meet their 'sanctuary' expectations. It may be very difficult, for example, for the wife to provide the kind of supportive domestic scene her husband requires at a time when she is beginning to feel insecure, when she is worried about the family's economic, education, and social future (Lewis and Cooper, 1990).

Not only is it difficult for a housebound wife to support her breadwinning husband and at the same time cope with family demands, but increasingly women are seeking full-time careers themselves. According to the US Department of Labor, the 'typical American family' with a working husband, a homemaker wife and two children now makes up only 7% of the nation's families. In fact, 44% of all married women are now working, as are 37% of women with children under six; in 1960 the comparable figures were 31% and 19%, respectively. It is claimed by many psychologists and sociologists that dual-career family development is the primary culprit of the very large increase in the divorce rate over the last 10 years in the United States and countries in Western Europe.

The problems this creates for the male workers are enormous, it affects almost all aspects of his life at work. For example, many professional men (eg managers) are expected, as part of their job, to be mobile, that is, to be readily available for job transfers, both within and between countries. Indeed, his promotional prospects depend wholly on availability and willingness to accept promotional moves. In the late 1980's and 1990's, as women themselves begin to pursue full-time careers as opposed to 'part-time jobs', the prospects of professional men being available for rapid deployment will decrease substantially. In the past, these men have, with few exceptions, accepted promotional moves almost without family discussion. Future such decisions will create major obstacles for both breadwinners in the family. We are already seeing this happen throughout Europe and the United States, and this is particularly exacerbated by the fact that corporations have not adapted to this changing social phenomenon. Few facilities are available in organisations to help either of the dual-career members of the family unit, particularly career break schemes (such as the recent Barclay Bank scheme).

Taking Action

With the increase in 'stress' litigation, and the escalating costs of employee health care insurance, more and more American companies are providing extensive health care, stress prevention and keep-fit programmes for employees. In the UK and Europe, however, only a few companies have flirted with stress prevention or counselling programmes—but mostly have either not tackled them seriously, or have abandoned their efforts. In addition, many company doctors and/or personnel managers who see the problems of stress at work have found it difficult to implement stress management courses and programmes— because senior executives feel that 'stress is none of our business', or 'he should be able to cope on his own', or 'our responsibility is to make profits for our shareholders, not to mollycoddle our employees'.

Even if organizations doubt the ethics of employee health care or stress prevention at work, they should see the 'cost-saving' argument in terms of lost work-days, absenteeism, poor perform- ance, premature death, retraining, etc. In the US, the cost argu- ments and the legal implications of cumulative trauma have weighed heavily in favour of primary prevention within companies. US organizations have used a number of different approaches towards stress prevention or health care; the pro- vision of 'keep-fit' facilities on site, dietary control, relaxation exercise classes, stress or psychological counselling, or some combination of these.

The health promotion and stress prevention schemes are as colourfully labelled as they are idiosyncratic in their orientation: 'wellness programme', 'treatment of chemically dependent employees', 'employee assistance programme', 'lifestyle change programme' and the like. It has been reported that the New York Telephone Company's wellness programme (ie cardiovascular fitness) saved the organisation $2.7 million in absence and treat- ment costs in one year alone. The giant copper corporation, Kennecott, introduced a counselling programme for employees in distress. This produced a drop in absenteeism of nearly 60 per cent on one year and a 55 per cent reduction in medical costs.

By far the most comprehensive and best researched of these programmes was undertaken by Control Data Corporation, one of the largest American computer companies. Like many major US firms, it is now 'self-insured'—covering its employees direct—and therefore has control of its own health care costs. Its programme is called STAYWELL. It is provided for the 22,000 Control Data employees and their spouses in 14 American cities as a 'free corporate benefit'. It has five components: stopping smoking, weight control, cardiovascular fitness, stress manage-

ment and improved diet (particularly, cutting down on cholesterol, salt and sugar). Each employee goes through three steps:

- A confidential health risk profile or screening is conducted.
  There is a comprehensive physical examination, but the
  employee also gives information on lifestyle and health
  behaviour (like smoking and drinking). This information is
  kept entirely confidential to the medical and nursing staff.

- Then employees attend an 'interpretation session'. Here
  they get their personal results and action plans to reduce
  their specific health risks.

- Finally, the employee selects the appropriate courses (on
  weight control or on stress management, for example),
  given his or her risk profile. Employee enrolment in the
  various Control Data Corporation schemes has ranged
  from 65 to 95 per cent at different sites throughout the US.
  Management and blue-collar workers participate equally.

But what is the outcome? The evidence is startling. Control Data
explored the 'average health care costs claims' of their employees,
and their 'hospital stays', and discovered:

- Employees who were encouraged to quit smoking spent
  half the number of days in hospital, and had 20 per cent less
  health care costs, compared with smokers.

- Those that underwent exercise training had 30 per cent
  fewer claims, and spent half the number of days in hospital,
  compared with the sedentary group.

- Most revealing of all, those employees who entered the
  cardiovascular fitness programmes, and reduced their
  hypertension levels, had less than half the health care costs
  of those who did not.

- In addition, when Control Data checked out the employees
  they rated 'most at risk' in terms of health habits (weight,
  stress, fitness, nutrition and smoking), they found that the
  high-risk employees were twice as likely to be absent from
  work due to sickness, and to be half as productive, as the
  low-risk or physically fit group.

In the UK, a number of organisations are beginning to realise the
enormous financial and human costs of stress; through poor

employee health, high sickness absence, high labour turnover, poor performance and lack of quality end-products/wastage. This realisation is only slowly turning into effective action. The majority of companies are only just 'toying' with the problem, putting on the occasional lecture on stress management or sending a personnel manager or occupational medic on a short course on stress awareness. Some forward thinking organisations, such as Cable and Wireless and Nestlé Rowntree are taking the problem more seriously and exploring stress as part of their regular medical screening. Many others are engaging Employee Assistance Programmes to help with stress counselling at work. The model of organisational stress audits, together with stress counselling at work is likely to lead the way for other companies and differing approaches. The task in Britain is urgent, if we are to adequately cope with the stress-related problems in industry of alcoholism, premature death due to heart disease, increasing sickness absence and worsening mental health among our workforce.

Conclusion

Workplace stress is likely to continue to present a major threat to the financial health and profitability of organisations. Growing health and safety legislation, escalating insurance costs and fear of litigation will increasingly force organisations to take a more responsible attitude toward stress reduction. And it is certainly the case that there is sufficient evidence from evaluative studies (Murphy, 1988) in the US and elsewhere that strategies for preventing stress and mental ill health in the workplace are not only useful but also pay dividends. As we indicated earlier, New York Telephone Company's stress prevention programme designed to improve cardio-vascular fitness saved the organisation $2.7 million in sickness absence and treatment costs in one year alone; General Motors reported a 40% decrease in lost time and a 60% decrease in accident and sickness benefits as a direct result of their programme; and even in the UK, the Post Office showed a saving of over 60% in sickness absence days from their stress counselling programme.

These secondary and tertiary levels of intervention have a useful role to play, but organisational preoccupation with the *outcome* of the stress process has tended to detract from the more proactive approach of addressing the *source* or causal factors in the stress process. Rather than focussing exclusively on what the organisation *can provide* for the employee to help them cope with the stress more effectively, employers would be well advised to consider what the organisation *can do* to eliminate or reduce workplace stressors. In the end, primary interventions and the diagnostic 'stress audit' are potentially more cost-effective and more focussed ways of reducing stress in the workplace.

References

Cooper, C. L., Mallinger, M. and Kahn, R. 'Identifying Sources of Occupational Stress Among Dentists'. *Journal of Occupational Psychology*, 51, 227–234, 1978.

Cooper, C. L. and Melhuish, A. 'Occupational Stress and Managers'. *Journal of Occupational Medicine*, 22, 588–592, 1980.

Cooper, C. L. and Davidson, M. and Robinson, P. 'Stress in the Police Service'. *Journal of Occupational Medicine*, Vol. 24, 1982.

Cooper, C. L. and Smith, M. *Job Stress and Blue Collar Work*. John Wiley & Sons, Chichester, 1985.

Cooper, C. L. and Payne, R. *Causes, Coping and Consequences of Stress at Work*. John Wiley & Sons, Chichester, 1988.

Cooper, C. L., Cooper, R. D. and Eaker, L. H. *Living with Stress*. Penguin Books, London, 1988.

Cooper, C. L. and Payne, R. *Personality and Stress: Individual Differences in the Stress Process*. John Wiley & Sons, Chichester, 1991.

Cox, T. *Stress*. Macmillan, London, 1978.

Crump, J. H., Cooper, C. L. and Smith, J. M. 'Investigating Occupational Stress: a Methodological Approach'. *Journal of Occupational Behaviour*, I, 191–202, 1980.

Dale, B. and Cooper, C. L. *Total Quality and Human Resources*. Blackwell Publ., Oxford, 1992.

Davidson, M. and Cooper, C. L. *Stress and the Woman Manager*. Blackwell Publ., Oxford, 1983.

De Frank, R. and Cooper, C. L. 'Worksite Stress Management Interventions'. *Journal of Managerial Psychology*, 2, 40–50, 1987.

Elkin, A. J. and Rosch, P. J. 'Promoting Mental Health at Work'. *Occupational Medicine: State of the Art Review*, 5, 739–754, 1990.

Ivancevich, J. M., Matteson, M. T. and Richards, E. P. 'Who's Liable for Stress at Work'. *Harvard Business Review*, March-April, 1985.

Kalimo, R., El Batawi, M. and Cooper, C. L. *Psychosocial Factors at Work and Their Relation to Health*. World Health Organisation, Geneva, Switzerland, 1982.

Lewis, S. and Cooper, C. L. *Career Couples*. Unwin Books, London, 1990.

Murphy, L. 'Workplace Interventions for Stress Reduction and Prevention'. In Cooper, C. L. and Payne, R. *Causes, Coping and Consequences of Stress at Work*. John Wiley & Sons, Chichester, 1988.

Sutherland, V. and Cooper, C. L. *Understanding Stress*. Chapman and Hall, London, 1990.

8

A STRATEGY FOR IMPROVING QUALITY OF WORKING LIFE

Campbell Ford

The Functions of the Advisory, Conciliation and Arbitration Service

ACAS is an independent statutory body with responsibilities for the improvement of industrial relations. Its most familiar functions are in the prevention and resolution of trade disputes by providing conciliation and arbitration services and in the promotion of conciliated settlements of actual or potential complaints to Industrial Tribunals. ACAS also provides advisory mediation services which are interventions designed to assist organisations and their employees to develop, for example, orderly bargaining or dispute procedures, improve communication or consultation practices or redesign reward systems.

Our statutory duties also include the provision of impartial advice, and the promotion of good industrial relations is our primary statutory obligation. This enables us to foster constructive and lasting relationships between employers and their employees and, of course, between their respective representatives. In this important function we seek to promote employee involvement and participation within the enterprise and to improve the quality of working life for people at all levels in the organisation. Although ACAS has no specific statutory obligations to have regard to the health, mental or otherwise, of the nation's workforce, this objective provides the locus for our interest in this topic. Certainly there can be no doubting the harmful effects of conflict and poor relationships on the state of mind of those involved, but it is now well recognised that the ways in which jobs are designed and work organised can impact just as much as management styles or difficult personal relationships. We would certainly concur with Cooper and Smith (1985) that 'Blue collar workers seem to be a vulnerable group to occupational stressors and their manifestations'.

The Context

The total cost to the nation of mental illness runs to many billions of pounds. According to the Department of Health it is a phenomenon largely associated with the adult population and affects the whole range of age and skill levels within the workforce. In terms of absenteeism alone the 80 million or so days lost due to mental health problems puts into context the half million lost due to strikes last year – and also the 26 million at the peak of the mining dispute in 1984. Statistics are helpful but they provide only a partial picture. There are a host of figures which are 'unknown and unknowable' [Deming] and it is impossible to gauge the effect on productivity of workers, who may feel alienated or simply de-motivated.

Good personal health, counselling programmes and planned measures to reduce stress levels all play an important part in the prevention of illness. However, the chances of their success will be greatly enhanced if the overall 'climate' is right and individual members of the workforce feel valued and respected. ACAS does not have a panacea to offer for the resolution of stress related illness but we are convinced that a good industrial relations climate is the starting point for any preventative strategy. We attempt to achieve this by encouraging organisations and their employees to embark on programmes designed to improve Quality of Working Life [QWL]. We believe that in doing so there will accrue to the enterprise considerable benefits in terms of effectiveness and competitiveness.

The Management of Conflict

Many of us have at some time or other experienced the tensions and pressures which arise from collective disputes and indeed these can be extreme – eg peer pressure to take industrial action, crossing picket lines, or involvement in subsequent disciplinary action. Whilst we accept that conflict may be endemic in the workplace most people are more comfortable if it is contained and managed; hence the complex machinery of industrial relations, of which ACAS is part. Certainly, the extreme perspectives, posited by Marx and others, of conflict and exploitation are less frequently encountered today. However, feelings of alienation, low esteem or simply low morale do still persist, not only in many of our large bureaucracies but also in the smaller organisations in which ACAS is often involved. Our pluralist traditions in Great Britain have taught us, by and large, to recognise and manage successfully divergent but legitimate interests. At least for a period there can be convergent interests and shared perspectives. We need to understand also, that although conflict does often exist it is not necessarily pathological. This is important in helping us deal with some of its adverse effects which manifest themselves in stress and associated problems. Indeed there are those who would suggest that industrial action and conflict actually release built up stress. However, long term hostility, confrontation and mistrust certainly must contribute significantly to the problems addressed by this conference.

Some, quoting strike statistics, might try to suggest that industrial relations problems have been 'resolved' in the 1980s. It would, however, be a mistake to take the incidence of strikes as the only indicator of the state of industrial relations. This is influenced more by overall economic factors which in turn affect trade union power at the workplace. On its own the incidence of strikes cannot be taken as a measure of good industrial relations between management and employees. Other indicators such as labour turnover, absenteeism or the level of internal grievances are much more revealing and an analysis of these can help identify potential stressors at the workplace. ACAS has acquired a reputation in the field of dispute resolution and inevitably we will continue to be called upon in the event of breakdowns in collective bargaining. But in our efforts to effect lasting improvements in industrial relations we attempt also to encourage a positive strategy which sets out to improve the quality of life of the employee and at the same time is one which has benefits in terms of operational effectiveness for the enterprise. In this approach the relationship between management and unions has to become one of partnership and many examples exist in all sectors of the economy. An alternative strategy of marginalising the trade unions may appeal to some but we believe this would create in the long run a void with no channel for the expression of dissent or machinery for managing conflict. This would be unfortunate not only for the successful management of stress but also, if we agree with the views of the Harvard school of economists (Rose and Wooley

1992), for greater economic efficiency. 'To some managers unions are part of the problem. In the most competitive countries they are part of the solution.' (Hoerr, Harvard Business Review 1991). For an example we need look no further than the successful cooperation between the powerful and influential union IG Metal and employers in the German manufacturing sector. We should not underestimate the importance of good relations between management and unions because this relationship is seen as a model by others in the workplace.

Workplace Stressors

It is generally accepted that some measure of stress can actually stimulate higher performance but over a certain level, however, the opposite effect occurs. And individuals have different thresholds. When we ask what are the main sources of stress and anxiety in the workplace the answers can be alarming. This may be because some practices have become institutionalised and others may be problems which persist in spite of management policies designed to eradicate them. From our observation some of the worst stressors include:—

* Insecurity or fear of redundancy.
* Autocratic management styles which are de-motivating and in the extreme are nothing less than 'bullying'.
* Erratic or inconsistent management strategies.
* Poor working conditions.
* Repetitive or boring work, often machine paced.
* Individual payment by result systems which demand a constant high level of performance to earn a living wage and sometimes at the risk to personal safety.
* Lack of opportunity to influence the way work is carried out – and the undervaluing of the employee's skill and talent.
* Poor communication processes – often in only the one direction and with little feedback of employees' views.

Many of these are stressful because they impact on individual living standards. Significantly, others lead to de-motivation and low morale since they are directly related to aspects of control and subordination of the workforce. These are all issues which a QWL strategy needs to address.

What is Quality of Working Life (QWL)?

A QWL strategy is an alternative to the management of people through a distorted Taylorist approach of tight measurement and control of work. Its main contributory strands are that:

* people will be better motivated if the work experience satisfies their social and psychological needs in addition to economic needs;

* individual motivation and therefore greater efficiency can be enhanced by attention to the design of jobs and work organisation.

* people work more effectively if they are managed in a participative way.

Quality of Working Life (QWL) is best understood if it is seen as a goal, as a process for achieving that goal and as a philosophy setting out the way people should be managed. As a goal, QWL aims to improve organisational effectiveness through the creation of more challenging, satisfying and effective jobs and work environments. As a process, QWL calls for efforts to realise this goal through the active involvement of people throughout the organisation. It is about organisational change usually from a 'control' to an 'involvement' organisation. The QWL philosophy views people as 'assets' capable of contributing skills, knowledge, experience and commitment, rather than as 'costs' that are merely extensions of the production process. It argues that encouraging involvement and providing the environment in which it can flourish produces tangible rewards for both individuals and organisations.

Quality of Working Life in Practice

The concept of QWL is not new. It is an approach to organising work and managing people that has evolved over a long period of time but unfortunately it has acquired some connotations of altruism and paternalism – largely due perhaps to the methods of introduction. The QWL approach is therefore a strategy rooted in the involvement and participation of people at all levels in the organisation. It recognises that management and employee representatives have a joint interest and a joint role in creating organisations that meet both business and human needs. This long-term strategy should provide an enduring set of best principles and practices designed to release the potential of people at all levels in an effort to establish the organisation as an efficient and competitive enterprise.

The key elements of a QWL organisation reinforce each other and include many or most of the following.

* A statement of organisation philosophy and values.
* A 'participative' management style.
* A flat organisational structure.
* QWL based job design and work structuring.
* Effective communications.
* Joint problem solving.
* Reward strategies focusing on the organisation, the group and skill acquisition.
* Selection processes emphasising individual attitudes and personal characteristics.
* A continuous process of training to match the QWL culture.
* 'Developmental' performance appraisal.

Job Design Principles

It is rarely possible for jobs to be designed to incorporate all the characteristics listed. Some will need to be traded off against others. Ideally however jobs should:

* form a coherent whole, either independently or with related jobs. Performance of the job should make a significant contribution to the completion of the product or service, a contribution which is visible to the job holder
* provide some variety of pace, method, location and skill
* provide feedback of performance, both directly and through other people
* allow for some discretion and control in the timing, sequence and pace of work efforts
* include some responsibility for outcomes
* provide some opportunity for learning and problem-solving (within the individual's competence)
* be seen as leading towards some sort of desirable future
* provide opportunity for development in ways that the individual finds relevant.

Management of Change

In the past ten years new technology and management techniques have dramatically transformed manufacturing companies as they bid to become internationally competitive. New ideas of Quality Management and cost saving 'Just in Time' techniques have been imported, via America, from Japan. In the service sector these ideas have taken hold and now many public sector managers are firmly committed to efficient and customer focused improvements. All this has considerable implications for all levels of the workforce. It is perhaps the process of change, inevitable as it is, that causes a high degree of emotion and strain. Apart from the obvious anxiety about possible job loss or skills becoming obsolete there are fears, especially amongst managers, about loss of prestige or reducing influence in a new organisational context: or simply the sincere belief that new aims or objectives constitute a betrayal of previous policies or commitments. Organisations who understand the QWL approach and where management and trade union are committed to it are well placed to tackle any programme of change. The advice of Moss Kanter is well put, in suggesting that we 'avoid creating losers' from the change – but if there are any, we need to be honest with them at an early stage. We also need to find time and the energy to reassure and to allow expressions of nostalgia and even grief for the past. When this is done we can then work to create excitement about the future.

Beware of Creating New Stressors

We must also remember that in the introduction of changes aimed at making the enterprise more effective or competitive, we will inevitably create additional or new stressors. These have to be minimised. For example, Statistical Process Control (SPC) can be intimidating to those who don't understand its purpose. And why should workers 'get it right first time' – if the systems are not right or they are inadequately trained or prepared? In the transfer from a management control culture to one of participation such as teamwork or self regulating work groups we need to be careful we are not simply exchanging one method of control for another. And peer pressure which I referred to earlier can be more demanding and more ruthless than enlightened management control. The TGWU (1989) identified stressors arising from new working practices and referred to methods of 'management by stress' and to 'parallel structures dominated by management prerogative'. New stresses also occur both for workers and managers in anxieties over their educational ability or training in being able to cope with new demands or skills required.

Practical Ways of Tackling Change Issues

In practical terms ACAS is capable of helping organisations in a number of ways that both enhance industrial relations and hopefully reduce work related stress by:

* giving general advice to both management and unions on job design and work organisation;
* providing examples of good practice;
* helping both managers and union representatives understand the concepts of new initiatives such as TQM and how they are likely to impact on industrial relations;
* helping in the design or the running of 'team building' events;
* and most importantly in facilitating working parties or workshop sessions focused on operational objectives and in managing some aspect of change.

Perhaps the most powerful method of encouraging active participation is in the 'workshop' where members of the workforce, their representatives and management get together to analyse operational objectives and consider appropriate methods for their achievement. For this employees need to appreciate the significance of new management initiatives, the emphasis on quality and customer care, and have an understanding of the different aspects of variability present in every process. This requires education and training in the use of the diagnostic tools such as flow charting, Pareto analysis and Statistical Process Control (SPC) – for which we are indebted to the TQ movement for emphasising their importance. Early active involvement in any process of change ensures ownership by the workforce and their unions and helps to allay many of their worst fears and anxieties. Inevitably ideas for changes in working practice emerge. Good job design, task rotation and teamworking ideas all contribute to the motivation of the workforce; and ACAS has much evidence which points to higher levels of job satisfaction in organisations which have taken on board these ideas. Teamworking and the use of primary production teams are becoming popular as are flatter hierarchies which facilitate the participative managerial approach advocated earlier. This enables easier and more fertile communication processes in organisations which are no longer 'compartmentalised'.

Conclusion

At many of the workshops which we have facilitated we have perceived excitement and sense of purpose of participants who for the first time in their working lives have been consulted or actively involved in discussing the work they undertake. They also produced significant suggestions for improvements in efficiency of the enterprise. The effect on the facilitator can also be exhilarating!

We do not seek to offer this QWL strategy as a panacea for all ills at the workplace; rather a set of mutually supporting principles designed to encourage involvement and participation of everyone. This we are convinced will produce benefits for the enterprise in terms of effectiveness; and for the individual, improved quality of working life. In tackling many of the issues which lead to stress at work we are also convinced that we play our part in the primary prevention of mental illness at work.

References

ACAS: Advisory Booklet No 16 (1991). *Effective Organisations: The People Factor*.

Cooper C. L. and Smith M. J. *Job Stress and Blue Collar Work*. 1985.

Deming W. E. (1982). *Out of the Crisis*, Cambridge University Press.

Hoerr J. *What Should Unions Do*. Harvard Business Review, May – June 1991.

Kanter, Rosabeth Moss. *The Change Masters: Corporate Entrepreneurs at Work*. London: Unwin, 1985.

Managing the Human Side of Change. Management Review, April 1985.

TGWU *Employee Involvement and Quality Circles*, 1989.

9

Secondary Prevention – Review of Counselling and EAPs

David A. Shapiro, Mark Cheesman, Toby D. Wall

Introduction

The past few years have seen vastly increased concern at the costs to British industry of mental health problems amongst employees. Managers increasingly feel they can ill afford the costs of reduced effectiveness and increased turnover amongst the workforce. A MORI poll of 112 of the top 500 UK companies showed that 65% of them believed stress was the major factor in ill-health for their organizations. The trend is toward seeing employees as whole persons whose overall well-being – expressed at work and beyond – has profound effects, for good or ill, on their job performance. We approach this sea change in attitudes from the sceptical viewpoint of applied scientists, by addressing four main questions:

1. How adequate is the evidence of mental health problems at work?

2. Why is this issue being taken more seriously now?

3. What can be done about it?

4. How useful are counselling and Employee Assistance Programmes (EAPs) as means of dealing with the problem?

We will devote most attention to the last of these questions.

Evidence of mental health problems at work

Recent evidence on the extent and costs of mental health problems in the workforce was well documented at the 1992 Department of Health/CBI Conference on Promoting Mental Health at Work, and readers are referred to the report of that conference for fuller information (Jenkins & Coney, 1992). For example, Jenkins (1992) reviewed epidemiological work on the general population in the community which showed that, in any one year, from 100 to 250 of every 1,000 adults have a psychological disorder. She also reviewed occupational studies, which tend to yield even higher estimates of the prevalence of mental ill-health amongst the workforce, possibly because such studies tend to be carried out where there is reason to believe rates are high (Wall & Clegg, 1981). In both general population and workforce, the most common disorders are depression and anxiety.

Warr (1992) summarised the characteristics of jobs which, when present in extreme form, have been found to have deleterious effects on psychological well-being and mental health. These include:

* low discretion or opportunity for control
* low use of skills
* high work demands
* low task variety
* high uncertainty
* low pay
* poor working conditions
* low interpersonal support
* low value in society

Another adverse factor is unsocial hours of work; the disruptive effects of shiftwork on biological rhythms as well as on everyday problems in living have increasingly recognised consequences for mental and physical health (Monk & Folkard, 1992).

Why is this issue being taken seriously now?

There are two main factors in the change of attitude towards mental health at work: first, the mounting evidence of the costs of the problem; and second, the growing realisation that something can be done about mental health problems at work.

Costs of mental ill-health at work

The costly consequences of mental illness for employer and employee alike have become increasingly clear (Banham, 1992). They include:

* increased risk of physical illness and death
* sickness absence
* labour turnover

* accidents
* impaired performance
* impaired relations with colleagues

Some of the adverse effects of mental ill-health at work may be due to the fact that mental illness produces difficulties in such non-work areas as:

* marital and family relationships
* personal finances
* looking after the home
* maintaining friendships

All these can serve to reduce an employee's commitment to or effectiveness at work. Employers thus have a direct interest in maximising the overall mental health and well-being of their workforce and can ill afford to neglect non-work problems experienced by employees.

Availability of preventive strategies

Only if remedies are available is there any incentive to recognise a problem. Until recently, the British 'stiff upper lip' culture derided counselling and psychotherapy as ineffective indulgence of the ineffectual individual. But as more and more employees, including senior managers, have direct personal experience of the benefits of counselling, this is increasingly seen as a practical and cost-effective means of overcoming stress at work. In addition, counselling and Employee Assistance Programmes (EAPs) have entered the UK business culture via their deployment within multinationals, and the burgeoning development of service providers.

What can be done about mental ill-health at work?

In contrast to the work of psychiatric specialists whose job it is to treat mentally ill patients referred to them, the remedies appropriate to the workplace are best viewed as prevention of such illness. There are two forms of prevention, primary and secondary.

Primary prevention seeks to reduce harmful effects of work or the workplace upon the mental health of the workforce. Attention is appropriately focussed on alleviating the extremes of the factors described by Warr (1992). For example, insufficient job discretion, the opportunity to make decisions about how to get the work done, is a primary source of unacceptable stress. This approach holds long-term promise, but the far-reaching changes required are unlikely to be achieved rapidly.

Our main focus is on *Secondary prevention*. This is work with individuals identified – by themselves or by the organization – as requiring help. Two main forms are available, worksite counselling and EAPs. We will describe each of these in turn, and discuss cultural and organizational issues in their implementation, before considering the research evidence on their effectiveness.

Employers may face a challenging choice between primary and secondary prevention strategies. For example, is it better to redesign jobs to increase opportunities for control or to provide counselling to those suffering depression as a consequence of lack of control? Such questions are wide open for research, which has yet to yield answers. Suffice it to say that there clearly are situations in which primary prevention is not possible, either because adverse job features cannot be changed, or because an individual's mental health problems have their primary origins outside work. Thus there will always be a need for secondary prevention strategies.

Worksite Counselling

Counselling includes a broad range of methods to help people learn new and more effective ways of coping with everyday stresses, which can lead to mental ill-health. There is no hard and fast dividing line between counselling and psychotherapy; some writers use the terms almost interchangeably, but they are best viewed as on a continuum, with counselling likely to be relatively brief and to deal with relatively mild problems as compared with psychotherapy.

A basic skill required of all counsellors is that of 'active listening', enabling them to understand more fully and attentively than in ordinary conversation the experiences and difficulties described by the troubled client. This is easier said than done, and can be misleadingly parodied as merely repeating back what the client has said.

How many counsellors does it take to change a light bulb? Only one, but the light bulb must want to change. In all seriousness, there is considerable skill in building the necessary relationship of trust between counsellor and client so that the client wants and feels able to change, and in accurately discerning the many layers of personal meaning contained in a troubled person's account of their difficulties. Sometimes the most important things are expressed indirectly. Without imposing their own view of a problem, the counsellor must actively help the client develop their own understanding of what is troubling them.

The process of forming a trusting relationship and reaching new understanding is often itself found to be helpful. In general, counsellors consider this to be a necessary first step, before moving on to consider what action the client might take to deal with the problem (Egan, 1986). At this point, counsellors offer a range of options. These may include:

* Relaxation and stress management
* Exercise programmes
* Sleep enhancement
* Alcohol, drug or eating disorder programmes
* Job-related skills
    (eg, delegation, time management)
* Personal skills
    (eg, assertiveness, interpersonal communication)
* Cognitive reappraisal
    (eg, assessment of personal control)

Counselling is a highly skilled business and requires extensive training. Counsellors come from a variety of backgrounds. Some may hold qualifications in cognate disciplines such as social work or clinical psychology. As discussed in the May 1992 issue of the British Association for Counselling (BAC) journal, *Counselling*, the accreditation of counsellors *per se* is developing rapidly. BAC accreditation requires appropriate basic training, compliance with an ethical code, and involvement in continuing training, development and supervision. The personal nature of counselling makes supervision particularly important, since isolated practitioners can easily make errors of judgment when personally challenged by the work.

Employee Assistance Programmes

An Employee Assistance Programme (EAP) uses a set of company policies and procedures to identify or respond to employees' personal or emotional problems which interfere directly or indirectly with job performance. It provides counselling, information, and/or referral to appropriate counselling treatment and support services. In essence, an EAP is a system for the timely, confidential, and non-prejudicial delivery of counselling to a workforce. In their systematic attention to organizational aspects of delivery, EAPs promise substantial benefits over and above a simple counselling service.

A large, centralized organization may choose to create an internal EAP by employing its own professionals, whilst a nationwide company with scattered workforce, or a smaller organization, may choose to contract with an external provider to supply EAP services. Other possible systems include union-based programmes and consortia of smaller organizations jointly contracting with an EAP. EAPs typically provide a blend of direct and short-term intervention, including rapid response via 24-hour helplines, and referral onward to other agencies. EAPs are a growing business. Employers considering investing in an EAP will want to be convinced of the likely benefits. We hope this article will help them ask the right questions.

Historically, EAPs arose during the 1940's from American employers' concern to reduce the effects of alcohol and drug abuse on the health and effectiveness of the workforce; their scope has been considerably broadened to cover any problem with actual or potential costs to the employer. American EAPs have spawned professional journals (eg, *Employee Assistance Quarterly*, *The Almacan*) and societies (eg, Employee Assistance Professionals Association). In what follows we have drawn extensively from reviews of EAPs in texts on job stress and applied psychology by MacLeod (1985), Murphy (1988), and Swanson and Murphy (1991).

Cultural and organizational issues in implementation

Several cultural and organizational issues are likely to determine the success or otherwise of employee counselling and EAPs. However, few of these have yet been directly researched.

Both counselling and the EAP concept originate from the USA. As proverbially noted by George Bernard Shaw, 'England and America are two countries divided by a common language'.

There are crucial cultural differences in attitudes to mental health as well as in the healthcare delivery system which argue against simply importing unmodified American-style EAPs into Britain.

Psychotherapy and counselling are much more prevalent and socially acceptable in the USA than in Britain. Consequently, American employees are more ready to acknowledge stress or mental health problems, and better-informed concerning the nature of counselling. Research shows that realistic and positive expectations on the part of clients are vital to ensure their productive engagement in counselling. This means that successful uptake of counselling services or EAPs by British workers cannot be taken for granted on the basis of American experience.

In addition, British employees think of the National Health Service as the main provider of healthcare; within the UK culture, the role of company doctors and private agencies in healthcare provision is less central than that of GPs and NHS specialist facilities. Combined with our greater reluctance to acknowledge personal problems at work, this may militate against uptake of worksite counselling and EAPs. Furthermore, an American EAP can reliably refer clients on for timely assistance from a variety of mental health services, provided only that the client is covered by adequate health insurance. In contrast, the NHS provides a narrower range of mental health services and immediate treatment may not be available. However, the greater resemblance of the 'reformed' NHS to the American system may reduce these cultural differences over the next decade.

From these considerations, it follows that the design and implementation of EAPs or counselling services requires adaptation for the UK workforce, and presentation in terms sensitive to UK norms, values and expectations, rather than simply following American practice. Employee perceptions should be assessed at each stage in the development of a programme and adjustments made accordingly.

Other organizational factors that are likely to be important to the success of any programme include:

* clear and explicit endorsement by all levels of management, and by unions, of a company policy to help employees to overcome personal problems and improve job performance

* no discrimination against those seeking professional help

* line managers and supervisors with skills to identify employees with problems and to help employees recognize their difficulties

* emphasis on voluntary participation, whether or not the manager or supervisor is the first to identify the need

* confidentiality seen by all within the company to be totally secure, with information released only with the client's written permission.

In contrast, the following militate against the success of a programme:

* weak support from top management or unions

* stigma attached within organization to those with emotional problems

* participation seen as a threat to job security

* managers and supervisors have no interest in facilitating appropriate use of the service

The decision to establish such a programme is not simply a commitment to spend so many thousand pounds per year. The decision represents no more than the end of the beginning of the company's efforts to deal with the problem of stress. There has to be continuing commitment to working on making the programme work – and that involves everyone in the organization.

Thus, setting up a secondary prevention system such as an EAP may well point to issues of primary prevention, as the shift in culture and climate required for a programme to be effective impinges on key features of jobs within the organization – such as discretion, demands or uncertainty – that determine employees' well-being and effectiveness. For example, consider a supervisor who is overworked, lacks control over use of time and is uncertain about how long an individual worker is to remain under their supervision. How effective will that supervisor be in identifying that individual's need for help and in discussing it sensitively with them?

Effectiveness of counselling and EAPs

Evaluation of counselling

What is the research evidence for the effectiveness of counselling? Regrettably, very few studies exist of worksite counselling per se. Our best, albeit provisional, estimate of effectiveness is obtained by reviewing a broad range of studies of counselling and psychotherapy carried out in mental health and educational settings (Lambert, Shapiro & Bergin, 1986; Shapiro, 1989). Typical findings reveal the average person receiving help to be better off, psychologically speaking, than up to three-quarters of those not receiving help. Our own research in Sheffield looks more closely at counselling with work-related problems, with similar results (Firth & Shapiro, 1986). Whilst these benefits are very worthwhile, research shows that average figures conceal wide variations, such that not all individuals receiving counselling will benefit substantially. There thus remains considerable room for improving the effectiveness of counselling.

In one of the few evaluations of worksite counselling, Cooper and Sadri (1991) examined a service within the British Post Office (Allinson, Cooper, & Reynolds, 1989; Welch & Tehrani, 1992). This was an open access service located within the occupational health service, staffed by clinical psychologists. Sickness absence and questionnaire data before and after counselling were compared, and these changes were set alongside those shown by a comparison group matched in terms of age, sex, grade, and years of experience.

Mental health and sickness absence improved substantially over counselling, typical of the counselling and psychotherapy literature. But, despite this improvement, the mental health and absence levels of the average client remained worse after counselling than that of a typical member of the comparison group. There were no changes in job attitudes over counselling. Reported health behaviours (not measured in the comparison group) changed over counselling, with decreased use of smoking, eating, coffee, and alcohol, and increased use of relaxation, exercise and humour.

There is thus promising evidence that worksite counselling is effective. However, most of the evidence is indirect, based on evaluation of similar methods in other settings, where the client and their presenting problems may be quite different from people seen at the workplace.

Evaluation of EAPs

Kim (1988) describes methods for evaluating EAPs. However, there are relatively few published EAP evaluation studies. They differ from research on counselling and psychotherapy in placing greater emphasis on cost savings rather than measures of psychological well-being. Most of these investigations suggest substantial benefits. We will summarise 3 typical studies.

The US Departments of Health and Human Services Employee Counselling Services (ECS) were the subject of a study by Maiden (1988). The EAP served over 150,000 employees through 16 geographically based divisions. Over 2,500 clients were seen over a 30-month evaluation period. They were compared with non-user employees matched for the agency in which they worked, sex, age and salary level. A cost-benefit analysis examined sick leave, absenteeism, and performance as assessed by supervisors. Average benefits of $1,274 per client were estimated over a six-month period, compared with an average EAP outlay of $991 per client seen. A five-year return of $7.01 per dollar invested was extrapolated from these figures, on the frankly untenable assumption that the level of benefit measured over 6 months would continue undiminished over 5 years.

An evaluation of the Ohio State EAP (McClellan, 1989) yielded more equivocal results. There were no benefits in terms of reduced accidents, theft, sick-leave, or turnover, or increased productivity. The sensitivity of these measures to EAP effects may have been diminished by State policies: for example, sickness absence was considered an entitlement to additional leave. In addition, the EAP itself was highly diffuse, comprising a central administrative and training unit, linked to 30 local community service centres, dealing in total with 44 health insurance plans and 86 service vendors. Accounting systems were imprecise and individuals' contacts with the EAP atypically long, suggesting later intervention than is ideal. In contrast, however, employees reported the high levels of satisfaction typical of all EAPs and counselling services.

The McDonnell Douglas Corporation's EAP combined the Corporation's internal EAP management with vendor-supplied assessment and referral professionals (Almacan, 1989). Absence and healthcare costs were assessed on an annual basis before and after each employee's participation in the EAP. Each EAP client was matched with 10 non-user employees on such factors as age, geographical location, gender, marital status, family size, and job code (but excluding psychological problems). Return on Investment (ROI) ratios of 3:1 and 4:1 were observed for clients seen in 1987 and 1988, respectively. Healthcare costs were consistently found to be much higher for non-EAP personnel than for EAP clients. These findings are impressive, and take no account of additional benefits, such as productivity, job performance, and the costs of carrying or replacing sick workers.

The varied results of these evaluations show that the cost-effectiveness of EAPs, whilst promising, cannot be taken for granted. The findings also point to factors conducive to success. For example, McDonnell Douglas' tightly managed and well-focussed EAP fared better than the more diffuse Ohio State programme.

Scientific issues

Although the results of evaluation studies are promising, they are not conclusive. As researchers, our confidence in the effectiveness of worksite counselling and EAPs is limited by methodological problems of the research done to date. The most important of these concerns absent or inadequate control groups.

It is well known that individuals seeking psychological help experience wide fluctuations from week to week, whether or not they receive help. Furthermore, they naturally tend to seek help when things are at their worst. Thus, any group of such people will tend to show improvement over time. To demonstrate the effectiveness of the help received requires comparison over a similar period of time with a control group of similar individuals not receiving help (Shapiro, 1989).

Some studies, such as those in the UK Post Office and the McDonnell Douglas Corporation, have included comparison groups not seeking help but matched for such factors as job level, age and sex. However, as demonstrated in the Post Office study (Cooper & Sadri, 1991), people not seeking help are much more psychologically healthy at the outset. This leaves much less room for improvement over time. So the fact that Cooper & Sadri's comparison group showed no change does not help us to attribute the improvement shown by those receiving counselling to the intervention itself. Studies in which individuals seeking help are assigned at random, either to immediate vs. delayed help, or to different kinds of help, are urgently needed.

Future directions

To enable worksite counselling and EAPs are to fulfil their promise for the UK workforce and economy, we urge developments in four areas: specification of guidelines and standards; adaptation to the UK environment; audit and evaluation; and service development.

Specification of guidelines and standards

In all human service domains, there is a strong trend towards the development of explicit procedural guidelines defining the standards of good practice. For example, the procedures to be followed in various forms of psychotherapy have been described in published 'manuals' and disseminated via audio or videotaped examples. Most of these appear readily applicable at the worksite. The more explicitly an intervention can be specified, the more readily it can be taught and evaluated. Furthermore, providing such explicit information in advance to clients renders counselling more effective (Orlinsky & Howard, 1986).

The organizational and delivery system aspect of EAPs, just as much as the counselling procedures delivered, can and should be standardised in this way. The Employee Assistance Professionals Association (1990, 1992) has published standards and professional guidelines. These cover programme design, implementation, management and administration, direct services, linkages with other agencies, and evaluation.

Adaptation to the UK environment

It is unwise to presume unthinkingly that American service methods and organizational designs are suited to the UK environment. For example, the manner in which American counsellors seek to communicate a genuine personal interest in clients can sound positively false to British ears. As already noted, other cultural, organizational and economic factors may profoundly affect the acceptability and effectiveness in Britain of programmes developed in the USA. The design of guidelines and standards for the UK environment must reflect these, and the success or otherwise of these adaptations must be carefully monitored.

Audit and evaluation

Worksite counselling and EAPs, being grounded within the behavioural sciences, lend themselves to thorough audit and evaluation (Kim, 1988), which will enhance their standing with organizations and lead to improvements in effectiveness, efficiency and quality of services delivered. However, the quality and quantity of published research is as yet insufficient.

Audit and evaluation should be built into all worksite intervention programmes; the results should be available to management in a form demonstrating the extent of the programme's success in meeting its objectives and identifying options for improving the service, without compromising the confidentiality of participating individuals.

Evaluation should begin with a thorough assessment of the nature and extent of need for services within the organization. This will inform subsequent appraisal of the programme's success in meeting identified needs. Approaches to evaluating and improving service delivery are described by Parry (1992) in relation to NHS psychotherapy services. These approaches are equally applicable to worksite counselling and EAPs, however. For example, Total Quality Management (TQM) is based on a management-led commitment to continual improvements in quality by improving existing processes and devising new and better ones.

However, audit and evaluation present problems that must be addressed from the outset of system design. For example, the costs of the evaluation itself have to be built into overall costings of any programme. Again, the potentially divergent or even conflicting values of stakeholders (such as the employing organization, the EAP agency, the counsellors it employs, the trade union representing the workforce, and the individual clients receiving counselling) must be adequately represented in the evaluation.

Service development

The services offered by worksite counselling and EAPs are not set in stone. Research and development will improve their acceptability, effectiveness and efficiency. For example, in Sheffield we have developed two forms of brief, structured counselling, comprising two sessions separated by a week, with a follow-up session three months later (Barkham & Shapiro, 1990). Within a format congruent with the resource levels and objectives of EAPs, this work offers a choice of two contrasting methods, according to the skills of the practitioner or the preferences or needs of the client.

Within this format, we have evolved a protocol for intolerant shiftworkers that explains to them the workings of the body clock and provides specific strategies for overcoming difficulties with sleep and the social and domestic consequences of working shifts (Taylor & Shapiro, 1993). We anticipate increasing demand for methods targeted on the needs of particular groups of workers.

We see great value in applying the methods of psychotherapy research to the development of worksite interventions. These interventions are no exception to the rule of widely varying effectiveness. To improve the overall success rate of counselling and EAPs, factors associated with good results must be identified. Following the lead of psychotherapy research (Garfield & Bergin, 1986), factors requiring analysis include the skills, methods and personal qualities of the counsellor, the capacity of the client to make use of help, and the organizational setting in which help is offered.

Psychotherapy research also offers ways of identifying the mechanisms underlying changes brought about by an intervention. For example, Reynolds, Taylor and Shapiro (1993) identified specific impacts reported by NHS employees after each of six sessions of a structured stress management training programme. Such process evaluations suggest which elements are helpful and how they achieve their effects. In turn, this enables the protocol defining an intervention to be improved.

Conclusion

Given widespread recognition of the costs of mental ill-health at work, demand for preventive intervention strategies is likely to increase. We see worksite counselling and EAPs as potentially very valuable. At this time, we endorse their use and development, which promises significant benefits to employing organizations and their workforce. However, we also consider that they can and should be substantially improved. We recommend close partnership between purchasing organizations, providers and researchers, focussed on the following objectives:

* specifying guidelines and standards for both service and organizational aspects

* adaptation of American methods and systems to the UK environment

* audit and evaluation to assess programmes in relation to guidelines and standards

* research and development to improve the quality, efficiency and targeting of interventions.

References

Allinson, T., Cooper, C. L., & Reynolds, P. (1989). Stress counselling in the workplace: Post Office experience. *The Psychologist, 12,* 384–388.

Almacan, The. (1989). McDonnell Douglas Corporation's EAP produces hard data. *The Almacan,* August, 18–25.

Banham, J. (1992). The costs of mental ill health to business. In R. Jenkins & N. Coney (eds.), *Prevention of mental ill-health at work: A Conference.* London: HMSO, pp 24–29.

Barkham, M., & Shapiro, D. A. (1990). Brief psychotherapeutic interventions for job-related distress: A pilot study of prescriptive and exploratory therapy. *Counselling Psychology Quarterly, 3,* 133–147.

Cooper, C. L., & Sadri, G. (1991). The impact of stress counselling at work. *Journal of Social Behavior and Personality, 6,* 411–423.

Egan, G. (1986). *The skilled helper.* (3rd Edn.). Monterey, California: Brooks/Cole.

Employee Assistance Professionals Association (1990). Standards for Employee Assistance Programs. 4601 N. Fairfax Drive, Suite 1001, Arlington, Virginia 22203, USA: EAPA.

Employee Assistance Professionals Association (1992). Standards for Employee Assistance Programs Part II: Professional guidelines. 4601 N. Fairfax Drive, Suite 1001, Arlington, Virginia 22203, USA: EAPA.

Firth, J., & Shapiro, D. A. (1986). An evaluation of psychotherapy for job-related distress. *Journal of Occupational Psychology, 59*, 111–119.

Garfield, S. L., & Bergin, A. E. (Eds.) (1986). *Handbook of psychotherapy and behavior change, 3rd Edn.* New York: John Wiley.

Jenkins, R. (1992). Prevalence of mental illness in the workplace. In R. Jenkins & N. Coney (eds.), *Prevention of mental ill-health at work: A conference.* London: HMSO, pp 1–23.

Jenkins, R., & Coney, N. (1992). *Prevention of mental ill-health at work: A conference.* London: HMSO.

Kim, D. S. (1988). Assessing employee assistance programs: Evaluation typology and models. *Employee Assistance Quarterly, 3*, 169–188.

Lambert, M. J., Shapiro, D. A., & Bergin, A. E. (1986). The effectiveness of psychotherapy. In S. L. Garfield & A. E. Bergin (Eds.), *Handbook of psychotherapy and behavior change, 3rd edn.* New York: Wiley, pp 157–211.

Macleod, A. G. S. (1985), EAPs and blue collar stress. In C. L. Cooper & M. J. Smith (eds.), *Job stress and blue collar work.* Chichester: John Wiley, pp 185–193.

Maiden, R. P. (1988). Employee assistance program evaluation in a federal government agency. *Employee Assistance Quarterly, 3*, 191–203.

McClellan, K. (1989). Cost-benefit analysis of the Ohio EAP. *Employee Assistance Quarterly, 5*, 67–85.

Monk, T. H., & Folkard, S. (1992). *Making shiftwork tolerable.* London: Taylor & Francis.

Murphy, L. R. (1988). Workplace interventions for stress reduction and prevention. In C. L. Cooper & R. Payne (Eds.), *Causes, coping and consequences of stress at work.* Chichester: John Wiley, pp 301–339.

Orlinsky, D. E., & Howard, K. I. (1986). Process and outcome in psychotherapy. In S. L. Garfield & A. E. Bergin (Eds.), *Handbook of psychotherapy and behavior change* (3rd Edn). (pp 311–381). New York: Wiley.

Parry, G. (1992). Improving psychotherapy services: Applications of research, audit and evaluation. *British Journal of Clinical Psychology, 31*, 3–19.

Reynolds, S., Taylor, E., & Shapiro, D. A. (1993). Session impact in stress management training. *Journal of Occupational and Organizational psychology*, **66**, 99–113.

Shapiro, D. A. (1989). Outcome research. In G. Parry & F. N. Watts (Eds.), *Behavioural and mental health research: A handbook of skills and methods*, chapter 9. Hove & London: Erlbaum.

Swanson, N. G., & Murphy, L. R. (1991). Mental health counselling in industry. In C. L. Cooper & I. T. Robinson (Eds.), *International review of industrial and organizational psychology volume 6*. Chichester: John Wiley.

Taylor, E., & Shapiro, D. A. (1993). Brief prescriptive counselling for shiftwork problems: A manual. University of Sheffield: SAPU Memo No 1396.

Wall, T. D., & Clegg, C. W. (1981). Individual strain and organizational functioning. *British Journal of Clinical Psychology, 20*, 129–130.

Warr, P. B. (1992). Job features and excessive stress. In R. Jenkins & N. Coney (eds.), *Prevention of mental ill-health at work: A conference.* London: HMSO, pp 40–49.

Welch, R., & Tehrani, N. (1992). Counselling in the Post Office. In R. Jenkins & N. Coney (eds.), *Prevention of mental ill-health at work: A conference.* London: HMSO, pp 67–82.

10

DEVELOPING CORPORATE MENTAL HEALTH POLICY

Ann Fingret

Introduction

All organisations in the UK employing more than 5 staff are required by the 1974 Health and Safety at Work Act to have a policy statement on health, welfare and safety. Some of the more enlightened employers have included a reference to mental health in this statement. The Health and Safety Executive have also issued a guidance note on Mental Health at Work.

In many, if not most, companies, activities directed towards health and welfare go little beyond the policy statement. Safety, with all the additional legislature, taking centre stage.

The best way to ensure that Management commitment to health as expressed in the general policy statement is implemented is to develop an overall Health Plan. The approach to mental health should be part of this general health plan. It may be necessary to have some special commitment to mental health since psycho-logical illness is still less well understood than physical illness. Management commitment should encompass not only the stated intention to enhance employee health but also the provision of resources to achieve this. This does require a degree of vision in that the cost/benefit equation has yet to be clearly demonstrated. It must be based on the somewhat elusive parameters of sickness absence, productivity, morale, turnover and customer service. Even when a commitment to health has been made by manage-ment and endorsed by unions, what each group actually believe they have bought may differ widely and is likely to be different again from the priorities as seen by an Occupational Health Consultant. It is obvious that the development of the plan will be facilitated by the existence of an in house Occupational Health Function. It is unlikely that it could be developed without at least access to Occupational Health advice.

The Health Plan inevitably includes both employee and organisational health. You really 'can't have one without the other'. The development of the plan will to some extent depend on whether one is in a green field site. Management awareness of human resource issues is now so widespread that it would be unusual to find no extant health-related policies.

Development

There are 3 stages of development.

   (1)   Audit

   (2)   Production of the Plan.

   (3)   Implementation

Audit

Auditing the structure of an organisation for issues related to mental health takes time. It is unlikely that the organisation is unique and therefore information about the health activities in other similar organisations will help to at least highlight areas that need to be addressed. It is also likely to highlight vast differences in resources and perspectives.

There really is no substitute for walkabout and for meeting key personnel. Over the assessment period, as ideas begin to be formulated, that can be tested out during the later group or individual discussions. It is very important not to form opinions too soon and to listen to the 'music behind the words'. It is helpful to develop some sort of mission statement which will be along the lines of 'To assist management in the development and maintenance of a healthy and efficient workforce'.

At the end of this stage, you will have gathered a considerable amount of information. Answers to the following questions should have been discovered.

(a) The Organisation:

   i)   What is the prevailing mores eg caring, 'macho'?

   ii)   Does the organisation appear to be 'in good health' to the employees and to the public at large?

   iii)   Are communications good?

iv)   Are there major organisational changes in progress or planned?

v)   Is management really committed to a Health Plan? What do they believe this to be?

vi)   Are the unions really committed to a Health Plan? What do they believe this to be?

vii) Is there any evidence of stress?

viii) What order of resource is likely to be made available to develop the Health Plan?

(b) Personnel Functions:

i)   What health-related policies are already in existence? for example, alcohol/smoking.

ii)   Are there adequate sickness absence statistics?

iii) What is the role of the personnel function? – management of resources and/or pastoral care.

iv)   How does Occupational Health stand in relation to personnel vis a vis such matters as confidentiality?

(c) Recruitment:

Nature of Work:

i)   Are there jobs with special physical or psychological requirements?

ii)   Are there jobs with known occupational hazards?

iii) What are the work patterns? If there are shifts how do they appear from psychological point of view?

iv)   What is the current mode of selection – is it the same for all staff? Is the health part confidential?

Company Policies:

i)   Does the company have relevant equal opportunity policies?

ii)   Are there facilities for people with disabilities?

iii) Does the company have superannuation hurdles?

iv)   Are most posts permanent or on limited contracts?

v)   What is the normal retirement age?

Results:

vi)   In what form is the result of any recruitment screening conveyed to personnel?

d) Sickness Absence:

    i)   Is there any formal procedure for monitoring sickness absence?

    ii)   Are there sickness absence statistics? – Are they expressed in an epidemiological form?

    iii)   What is the arrangement for sick pay? Is it the same for all groups of staff?

    iv)   What is the organisation's approach to temporary light work or other form of modified duty?

e) Termination on Grounds of Ill Health – 'Medical Retirement'

    i)   What are the organisation's rules on superannuation and early retirement?

    ii)   How flexible is the organisation in accommodating these?

    iii)   What is the role of the organisation's medical adviser in these matters?

f) Health Hazards

    i)   What is there in the way of potentially hazardous work – chemical, physical or biological?

    ii)   What arrangements are in place to protect employees?

g) Safety Management

    i)   Are safety professionals employed? If so, what is the thrust of their activities?

    ii)   How does the safety organisation relate to the Occupational Health establishment?

    iii)   In general, how well are procedures and policies followed?

    iv)   is there a consultative structure?

    v)   Is there a safety management structure?

h) Occupational Health

    i)   How many Occupational Health Staff are in place? What are their qualifications?

    ii)   At what level does the Senior Occupational Health incumbent report?

    iii)   What is the present cost of any health provision per capita?

    v)   If there is no Occupational Health Service, what is the source of health advice?

i) Health Promotion/Health Screening

    i)   Are there any internal health promotion, screening
         activities?
    ii) Who provides them?
    iii) Which sections of the workforce is offered these facilities?

j) Training

    i)   Is there a training function?
    ii) What aspects of health are included in the training
         programme?
    iii) Is Occupational Health involved in general management
         training?

Producing the Plan:

You should now be able to define the needs of the organisation in
relation to the current provision. The emphasis of any Health Plan
will obviously differ according to the nature of the business.
There is clearly a difference between the needs of a chemical
company to that of a service industry. But this difference is likely
to be in emphasis rather than overall content.

The plan should cover the following areas: – *see Table 1.*

TABLE 1: *Content of Health Plan*

Selection of Staff
Training – Management
          – General Lifeskills
Management of Change
Personnel Policies: Sickness Absence/Rehabilitation/Retirement
Substance Abuse
Counselling/Support Groups
Audit

Selection of Staff:

It goes without saying that there are 'horses for courses' and that
the right person in the right job is a recipe for well-being. It is
traditionally very difficult for individuals who have experienced
a psychiatric illness to obtain employment. The role of the
Occupational Physician is not to exclude people but to ensure that
they are placed in suitable posts and given any necessary support
and supervision. But as with general recruitment, it may be very

difficult to ensure a person/job fit. How to obtain a good person/job fit is far from clear. There is little evidence that the batteries of psychological tests available are of any use, except perhaps in organisations with special personnel needs such as police forces.

Most organisations that use personality tests on recruitment do not really have a clear idea of the 'perfect' employee. The general interview situation should at least give the opportunity of assessing whether the individual would 'fit' the organisational style.

Training:

a) **Management Training**

i) Human Resource Management Skills:

The ability to manage does not come naturally. There are still many managers who have received no training in human resource management skills such as those listed in Table 2.

TABLE 2: *Management Skills*

regular/open communication with staff
being able to delegate
being able to make decisions
fair criticism
fair appraisal

ii) Recognition and Management of Stress:

Part of any general training programme for managers should include recognition of maladaptive behaviour in themselves and in their staff and techniques for dealing with both. Normally described as 'recognition and management of stress'. Typically this training is carried out in a workshop format.

b) **General Training**

Not only do managers need to be trained to manage themselves and their staff but all individuals in an organisation can benefit from lifeskills training. Such training enables individuals to make healthy choices for physical and mental health, to express their views in an assertive way, to manage their time appropriately and to understand the dynamics of relationships.

c) **Management of Change:**

If major change is envisaged in the workplace, a strategy should be developed to minimise the adverse effects on staff. No one likes change. A successful and unhurtful change process depends on the factors listed in Table 3.

TABLE 3: *Factors important for successful management of change*

good communications
realistic timing
clarification of issues
clarification of choices
counselling support including career guidance.

Managers need to know how to manage change, how to change 'no' to 'yes'. Too often major change finds managers beleaguered with no skills or time resources to negotiate the change period successfully either for themselves or their staff. Planning is essential.

Development of Special Policies:

Sickness Absence

No matter how well an organisation and its health provision is organised, there will be people who become mentally ill. This will range from short duration stress disorders to psychotic illness.

The organisation's Sickness Absence Policy should encompass its position on rehabilitation and resettlement in a general way. Because mental illness is less well understood and because the pre-absence behaviour may have been disturbing or even bizarre, a particular effort may have to be made by Occupational Health staff in conjunction with the patient's own doctor, to bring the patient successfully back into the work setting. Re-entry may provoke either considerable resistance on the part of work colleagues or, for the best possible reasons, over-protectiveness resulting in an unwillingness to let the individual get on with the job.

Alcohol

Another important relevant special policy is one relating to alcohol abuse.

Table 4   Alcohol Policy

Restriction of availability
Management Training
Health Education
Clear Personnel Procedures
Job Security

An Alcohol Policy should include, as near as possible, total restriction of alcohol on the premises. It should also encompass training of managers and staff in the recognition and management of alcohol abuse. The procedures for dealing with someone with an apparent alcohol problem should be clear. Essential to any such policy is the opportunity of paid sick absence to receive treatment and the guarantee of a secure post. Both these factors will make it more likely that those with an alcohol problem feel able to seek help.

Provision of Counselling Facilities:

The range and type of counselling facilities vary enormously between organisations. The range is usually determined more by the available resources and company style than by the overall need.

Counselling is not easily available within the NHS, however, very few UK organisations have anything but a fledgling counselling service. This may be provided by Personnel or Occupational Health or in a minority of cases, by a trained counsellor or social worker. Some organisations have arrangements with external counselling agencies to the extent of a full blown employee assurance programme. Counselling is usually better if provided by counsellors outside the management structure but not outside the organisation, except in specialist areas such as alcohol abuse.

Counselling at an early stage can and does reduce employee distress, poor performance and sickness absence. ATT, for example demonstrated a 2% reduction in sickness absence as a result of their comprehensive Employee Assistance Programme.

Audit of Organisational Health:

The Occupational Health team may be very well placed to identify departments or even aspects of the whole organisation which are unhealthy. The team is likely to see a complete cross-section of staff and will certainly be the recipient of complaints and anxieties.

Of course, there are well-recognised parameters of organisational sickness:

Table 5 Signs of Organisational Ill-Health

high staff turnover
poor staff morale
customer complaints
reduced productivity
increased sickness absence

The Occupational Health team may also have access to tools such as the Occupational Stress Indicator which can be used to analyze sources of stress in work groups. On-going assessment of individual groups by Occupational Health may prove to be a very successful way of taking the organisation's temperature.

Summary

Steps in the development and implementation of a mental health plan in line with the policy statement are:

- Assess the needs by use of internal or external Occupational Health professionals.
- Ensure fair selection procedures.
- Provide good management training to incorporate stress management and change management.
- Provide lifeskills training for the workforce.
- Set up systems to assess the health of the organisation and of individual units.
- Develop policies of sickness absence to enable rehabilitation.
- Develop re-settlement policies.
- Develop substance abuse policies.
- Provide information on or access to confidential counselling.
- Develop self-support groups for special needs.

11

CONCLUSIONS

Patrick McLoughlin

Introduction

Ladies and gentlemen, I am very pleased to have been asked to make the closing speech at this conference. Not least because it gives me the opportunity to emphasise the importance of the subject you have been discussing today. By attending the conference you too have recognised its importance. And you have recognised too that you have a part to play in tackling this problem, in the workplaces for which you are responsible.

I propose today to focus on just one aspect of mental health at work. But it is one of the most significant in its effects both on individuals and on industry generally. I am talking about stress. I am not thinking of those employees who welcome a degree of 'pressure' and work better for it. I am thinking of those who become overwhelmed by excessive or extended periods of pressure at work.

I will look at three main areas: the effects of stress at work; what those of you who are employers or managers can do to *ease* stress in the workplace; and what help you can provide for employees who are suffering.

Let me start with some statistics.

- A MORI poll of 112 of the top 500 companies showed that 65% of them believed stress was the major factor in ill health for their organisation.

- A CBI survey of 200 companies showed that work stress, poor motivation, and drink related problems were seen as the three main factors related to absenteeism.

- The CBI estimate that thirty days are lost to stress for every single day lost to industrial action.

Effects of Stress

All of this demonstrates just how severe a problem stress can be in the workplace. Recognising the signs as early as possible is vital. Stress can reveal itself in many ways. Some of these may not, on the surface, seem directly attributable to stress.

For example, stress can cause sickness absence due to physical illness. This is because it lowers the body's resistance. It can lead to ineffective working – stressed employees may take poor decisions and make mistakes, or develop poor timekeeping and attendance records. And stress can contribute to poor working relationships with colleagues, and customers.

And if we add in the link between stress and misuse of alcohol or drugs, there is an obvious risk of stressed employees making errors. These errors can have dire consequences for the safety of others.

What an Employer can do

Of course, it may be a combination of domestic or personal factors, as well as work-related ones, which cause an individual stress. But even where the underlying cause is not to do with work, the individual under stress will be more susceptible to workplace stress. So, what can an employer do to minimise the effects of stress?

The first principle must be to have good communications in the workplace. Ensuring staff are kept informed about any major changes that are taking place in the business. One of the greatest causes of workplace stress for employees is not knowing what's going on and how it affects them.

Research has also shown that another major cause of stress in the work place is employees not knowing what is expected of them. This is particularly true of staff in lower grades who have less control over the work they do. A second basic principle, then, is to ensure that employees have proper job descriptions and clear work objectives.

Thirdly, employers need to ensure that work is organised so that employees have proper managerial support and adequate training for the tasks they have to carry out. Lack of managerial support, levels of responsibility which are too high or too low, isolation and lack of involvement, and insufficient training for the job have all been shown to increase the likelihood of stress.

Finally, individual job design can also be important. While some employees enjoy repetitive work, others can find it stressful. Job rotation, widening the duties within a particular job and increasing the personal control an individual has over the planning and organisation of their work can all be beneficial.

Help for Employees

All these principles, basic though some of them may seem, should go a long way to minimising the risk of harmful stress in the workplace. But if, despite your best efforts, someone shows signs of stress, what can you do? Where can you go for help?

Employers can actually do quite a lot. In the first place, it is important that employees suffering from stress are dealt with sensitively. Often it is best to let such employees talk through their problems with someone outside the management structure in a confidential and sympathetic environment. Some of the most effective counselling can be that provided by colleagues with similar experiences.

If resources allow, such counselling can be fitted into a general health care programme. This will enable staff to improve their general health and fitness, and be more able to cope with the challenges of work. Other elements of such a programme can include advice on life styles, healthy eating and drinking, giving up smoking, and the use of relaxation techniques. As you will have learned this afternoon, a small but increasing number of UK companies are also making use of 'employee assistance programmes.' The Health and Safety Executive is currently funding a research project to assess and measure the effectiveness of these programmes and to identify the characteristics of those which are successful. Some companies also have their own occupational health service which will be able to provide guidance to both the employer and employees.

My own Department offers a free and confidential counselling service to all staff. All counsellors receive full training and, in some cases, our counsellors are qualified occupational psychologists. Counselling covers both work-related and personal issues.

Training, too, has an important role in preventing and alleviating stress. Courses on time management and techniques such as assertiveness, on how to recognise stress and how to deal with it, can all play a part.

But health care, counselling and training are no substitute for removing unnecessary occupational stress, or controlling it if removal is unrealistic. It is no good returning staff who have suffered occupational stress to face the same unnecessary stressors which caused the problems in the first place.

Some of you, especially those involved with small businesses, may be concerned about the amount of time and money needed to provide the kind of help I have been outlining. I can say to you that the best solutions are often the cheapest and simplest. There is often no need to invest in expensive health care systems.

It is important that employers examine carefully why and how stress may be affecting their employees so that they can develop strategies which are appropriate to their particular needs. This is the most practical and cost-effective way forward.

As a first step, the Health and Safety Executive can provide advice. For example, it has produced a free guidance booklet 'Mental Health at Work'. It describes some of the factors that can affect mental health at work and what employers can do to develop and promote sound mental health policies. Employers can also obtain advice direct from the HSE's Employment Medical Advisory Service, EMAS. EMAS is a team of doctors, nurses and others, trained in all aspects of occupational health. They provide advice not only to employers but to the Careers Service and Employment Service on the training and re-training of people who have health problems – including mental health problems.

Closing

I don't suppose that any of us is in any doubt that stress at work is costly to businesses, both in terms of lost production and its effects on staff. My hope is that today's conference has provided you with the means to do something about it – not only in terms of influencing policy, but by taking practical steps to minimise stress in the workplace, and to help those suffering to overcome it.

ORGANISATIONS REPRESENTED AT THE CONFERENCE

Abbey National plc
Advisory Conciliation and Arbitration Service
Applied Psychology Research Group
ASE (A Division of NFER-NELSON)
Bank of England Registrars Department
Barclays Bank plc
BBA Group plc
BICC Cables Ltd
Bloomsbury and Islington Health Authority
British Airways
British Aerospace Military Aircraft
British Aerospace
British Gas plc
British Gas (South Western)
British Gas (Wales)
British Rail
British Telecommunications plc
Cambridgeshire County Council
CBI
Chichester Health authority
Commercial Union plc
Corecare Ltd
Counselling in Primary Care Trust
Department of Health
Department of Trade and Industry
Derbyshire County Council
Employee Assistance Professionals Association
Employment Service
English National Opera
Essex Rivers Healthcare Trust
Esso Petroleum Co Ltd
Forbo Kingfisher Ltd
GEC

Girobank plc
Goodyear (GB) Ltd
Guinness plc
Guinness Brewing Worldwide
Hay Management Consultants
Health & Safety Executive
Health Education Authority
Health & Safety Commission
Hickson International plc
Hill Taylor Dickinson
IHSM Consultants
Ilford Ltd
Institute of Personnel Management
J Sainsbury plc
Joint Research and Health Advisers
Kodak Limited
Lancaster Priority Services NHS Trust
Lever Brothers
Lewisham and North Southwark H A
London Transport Medical Service
Manchester School of Management
Margery Povall Associates
Marks & Spencer plc
Medisure Marketing and Management Ltd
Mid Southern Water plc
Mid Glamorgan County Council
Mid Glamorgan County Council
Midland Bank
National Association for Staff Support
NHS Health Advisory Service
North Nottingham Health Authority
North Derbyshire Health Authority
North Devon Health Promotion
Northamptonshire County Council
Northern Health and Social Services Board
Nottingham Community Health
Nuclear Electric plc
Nurses Pay Review Body
Personal Performance Consultants UK Ltd
Personal Performance Consultants
Price Waterhouse

Priory Hospitals Group
RELATE Marriage Guidance
Remploy
Remploy Ltd (Direct Training Division)
Royal National Institute for the Blind
royal Marsden Hospital and Institute of Cancer Research
Royal College of Psychiatrists
Schering Agrochemicals Ltd
Shell UK Ltd
Shropshire Mental Health NHS Trust
SmithKline Beecham Pharmaceuticals
Solihull Healthcare
Solihull Health Authority
South East London Health Promotion Service
South West Thames Regional Health Authority
South East Kent Health Authority
South Birmingham Health Authority
Southern Derbyshire H A
Southmead Health Education Department
St George's Hospital Medical School
Stress Solutions Ltd
Surrey County Council
The University of Westminster
The Reader's Digest Association Ltd
The Mental Health Foundation
The Royal Marsden Hospital
The Associated Octel co Ltd
The Wellcome Foundation
The Dukes Priory Hospital
Theodore Goddard
Thomas Cook Group Ltd
Trade Union Congress
Trent Health
Trent Regional Health Authority
UBAF Bank Ltd
Unilever plc
Unipart Group of Companies
United Biscuits (UK) Ltd
University of Leeds
University of North London
University of Sheffield

University of Warwick
Voula Grand Consulting
Wessex Regional Health Authority
Wessex Water plc
West Essex Health Authority
West Sussex County Council
Westpac Banking Corporation
Yorkshire Electricity
Zeneca Ltd

Printed in the United Kingdom for HMSO
Dd296388 7/93 C13 G531 10170